STANDARDS-BASED

WITHDRA

S0-BDW-321

WORD BY WORD BASIC

Second Edition

Steven J. Molinsky • Bill Bliss

Contributing Authors
Elizabeth Handley
Janet Gokay
with
Sharon Carlson
Jill Goodsell

PEARSON
Longman

Word by Word Basic Lifeskills Workbook

Copyright © 2009 by Pearson Education, Inc.
All rights reserved.
No part of this publication may be reproduced, stored in a retrieval system, or transmitted
in any form or by any means, electronic, mechanical, photocopying, recording, or otherwise,
without the prior permission of the publisher.

Pearson Education, 10 Bank Street, White Plains, NY 10606

Editorial director: Pam Fishman
Vice president, director of design and production: Rhea Banker
Director of electronic production: Aliza Greenblatt
Director of manufacturing: Patrice Fraccio
Senior manufacturing manager: Edith Pullman
Marketing director—adult and higher education: Oliva Fernandez
Senior digital layout specialist: Lisa Ghiozzi
Production editor: Diane Cipollone
Text design: Wendy Wolf
Cover design: Tracey Munz Cataldo, Warren Fischbach
Realia creation: Warren Fischbach, Lisa Ghiozzi
Illustrations: Richard E. Hill

ISBN 978-0-13-200357-5; 0-13-200357-0

PEARSON LONGMAN ON THE WEB
Pearsonlongman.com offers online resources
for teachers and students. Access our
Companion Websites, our online catalog,
and our local offices around the world.

Visit us at **pearsonlongman.com**.

Printed in the United States of America
1 2 3 4 5 6 7 8 9 10—DOW—12 11 10 09 08

CONTENTS

A INFORMATION ON AN ENVELOPE

Look at the envelope. Match the information.

> Anita K. Wilson
> 17 Elm Street, Apt. 3C
> Miami, FL 33140
>
> US

_d_	1. first name	a.	3C
___	2. city	b.	Wilson
___	3. apartment number	c.	Florida (FL)
___	4. last name	d.	Anita
___	5. zip code	e.	K.
___	6. state	f.	Miami
___	7. address	g.	33140
___	8. middle initial	h.	17 Elm Street, Apt. 3C

B ANITA'S REGISTRATION FORM

Complete the registration form with Anita's personal information on the envelope above.

REGISTRATION FORM

NAME	FIRST Anita	MIDDLE INITIAL
	LAST	

MAILING ADDRESS

NUMBER	STREET	APT. #
CITY	STATE	ZIP CODE

C ADDRESSING AN ENVELOPE

Interview a classmate. Then fill out the envelope below with the classmate's name and address.

US

_____
_____
_____

Look at the registration form. Match the information.

REGISTRATION FORM

NAME	FIRST Alan	MIDDLE INITIAL H.	LAST Park

ADDRESS	NUMBER STREET 56 Ocean Drive	APARTMENT 4D	CITY San Diego	STATE CA	ZIP CODE 92102

TELEPHONE 619-267-5890   CELL PHONE 619-379-2688

E-MAIL ADDRESS alan22@hmail.com   SSN 295-72-0932

DATE OF BIRTH 3/21/85   PLACE OF BIRTH Brooksville, FL   SEX ☒ M ☐ F

_d_ 1. place of birth
____ 2. telephone number
____ 3. date of birth
____ 4. sex
____ 5. cell phone number
____ 6. social security number
____ 7. e-mail address

a. 295-72-0932
b. 3/21/85
c. male
d. Brooksville, Florida
e. 619-267-5890
f. 619-379-2688
g. alan22@hmail.com

Fill out the form with YOUR personal information.

REGISTRATION FORM

NAME	FIRST	MIDDLE INITIAL	LAST

ADDRESS	NUMBER STREET	APARTMENT	CITY	STATE	ZIP CODE

TELEPHONE   CELL PHONE

E-MAIL ADDRESS   SSN

DATE OF BIRTH   PLACE OF BIRTH   SEX ☐ M ☐ F

Reaching Out!

A Registration Form for a Classmate

Make a new registration form. Interview a classmate and fill out the form with your classmate's personal information.

A ROSA'S FAMILY

Rosa is ten years old. These are pictures of Rosa's family. Label the pictures for Rosa.

| my brother | my father | my grandmother | my grandfather | my mother | my sister |

1. _____my mother_____

2. _____

3. _____

4. _____

5. _____

6. _____

B MALE OR FEMALE?

Look at page 5 of the Basic Picture Dictionary. Which words are male? Which are female? Which are male and female?

Male	Female	Male and Female
husband	wife	parents

Who are the people in your family? Draw or bring to class pictures of the people in your family and label the pictures. Then tell a classmate about your pictures.

Reaching Out!

Your Family Pictures

C WHO ARE THEY?

_c_ 1. My mother and father are my ____.

____ 2. My son and daughter are my ____.

____ 3. My grandmother and grandfather are my ____.

____ 4. My grandson and granddaughter are my ____.

____ 5. My sister and brother are my ____.

a. grandchildren

b. grandparents

c. parents

d. siblings

e. children

D A FAMILY TREE

Look at the family tree and choose the correct answer.

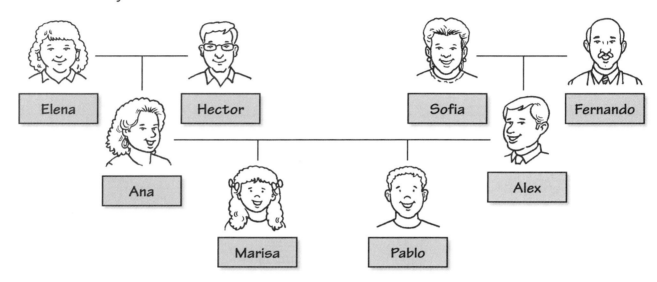

1. Marisa is Pablo's ((sister)   wife).
2. Ana is Marisa and Pablo's (mother   father).
3. Pablo is Alex and Ana's (daughter   son).
4. Marisa is Hector and Elena's (grandson   granddaughter).
5. Fernando is Pablo and Marisa's (grandfather   father).
6. Alex is Ana's (husband   son).
7. Alex is Marisa and Pablo's (brother   father).
8. Sofia is Fernando's (mother   wife).
9. Ana is Hector and Elena's (daughter   son).
10. Pablo is Marisa's (son   brother).
11. Ana and Alex are Pablo's (parents   grandparents).
12. Sofia is Pablo and Marisa's (granddaughter   grandmother).

Reaching Out!

Your Family Tree

Draw a family tree diagram of your family and label the people's names. Show your family tree to a classmate and tell about it.

A WHO ARE THEY?

Look at the pictures. Write the correct word.

| brother-in-law | cousin | nephew | niece | sister-in-law | uncle |

my brother's family

a. my brother
b. my ___sister-in-law___
c. my _____

my sister's family

d. my sister
e. my _____
f. my _____

my aunt's family

g. my aunt
h. my _____
i. my _____

B GREG AND JULIE'S FAMILY

Greg and Julie are husband and wife. Look at Greg's family tree and choose the correct answers.

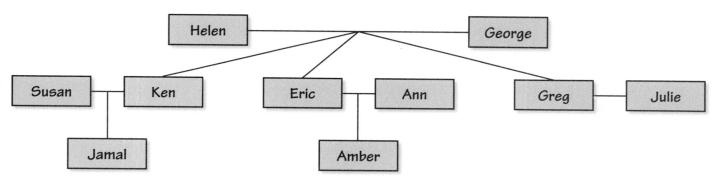

1. Helen is Greg's ((mother) sister).
2. Helen is Julie's
    (mother-in-law sister-in-law).
3. Eric is Greg's (uncle brother).
4. Eric is Julie's (uncle brother-in-law).

5. Jamal is Greg's (nephew cousin).
6. Jamal is Julie's (son-in-law nephew).
7. Ann is Greg's (sister sister-in-law).
8. Ann is Julie's (aunt sister-in-law).

Reaching Out!

Your Relatives

Bring in pictures of your relatives and tell about them. Where do they live? What do they do? How many aunts, uncles, cousins, nephews, and nieces do you have? Talk about your relatives with a classmate.

Luisa's Registration Form

International Language School
1542 Washington Street
Los Angeles, CA 90187

REGISTRATION FORM

NAME FIRST Luisa MIDDLE INITIAL M. LAST Sanchez **DATE** 9/15/09

ADDRESS NUMBER 159 STREET Carter Street APARTMENT 23 CITY Los Angeles STATE CA ZIP CODE 90189

SEX ☐ M ☒ F **TELEPHONE** (323) 457-8490 **CELL PHONE** (323) 457-8813

E-MAIL ADDRESS luisas@eworld.com **SOCIAL SECURITY NUMBER** 146-67-8032

DATE OF BIRTH 8/15/91 **PLACE OF BIRTH** Mexico City, Mexico

OTHER FAMILY MEMBERS AT INTERNATIONAL LANGUAGE SCHOOL? YES ☒ NO ☐

WHO? Roberto Sanchez (cousin), Isabel Mendoza (aunt)

1. Luisa's last name is _____.
   a. Carter
   b. Sanchez
   c. Mendoza

2. Luisa's address is _____.
   a. luisas@eworld.com
   b. 1542 Washington Street
   c. 159 Carter Street

3. Luisa's date of birth is _____.
   a. 9/15/09
   b. 8/15/91
   c. Mexico City

4. Luisa's social security number is _____.
   a. 146-67-8032
   b. 323-457-8813
   c. 90189

5. M is Luisa's _____.
   a. sex
   b. surname
   c. middle initial

6. 323 is Luisa's _____.
   a. street number
   b. area code
   c. apartment number

7. Luisa's aunt and _____ are at the International Language School.
   a. brother
   b. cousin
   c. uncle

8. Luisa is Isabel Mendoza's _____.
   a. niece
   b. nephew
   c. cousin

CLASSROOM OBJECTS

A THE SUPPLY CLOSET

What's in the supply closet? Look in the supply closet and check what's there.

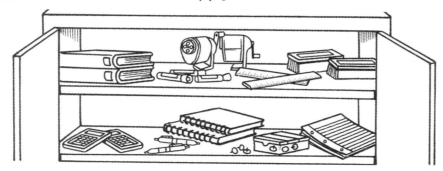

☐ binders	☐ thumbtacks	☐ calculators
✓ pencil sharpeners	☐ textbooks	☐ chalk
☐ pens	☐ workbooks	☐ graph paper
☐ rulers	☐ pencils	☐ markers
☐ spiral notebooks	☐ erasers	☐ notebook paper

B MARTIN'S DESK

What's on Martin's desk? Fill in the correct words.

eraser   graph paper   keyboard   monitor   mouse   pencil   printer   ruler   workbook

a. ___printer___   d. _____   g. _____

b. _____   e. _____   h. _____

c. _____   f. _____   i. _____

Look at pages 8 and 9 of the Basic Picture Dictionary. Make a list of the classroom objects that you have at school today. Make a list of the classroom objects that you have at home. Compare with a classmate.

Reaching Out!

*At School and
At Home*

THE CLASSROOM

A TWO CLASSROOMS

Compare the two classrooms. Write the items you see in the correct circles below.

bookcase	clock	globe	teacher's desk
bulletin board	computer	map	wastebasket
chairs	desks	table	whiteboard

Classroom 1

Classroom 2

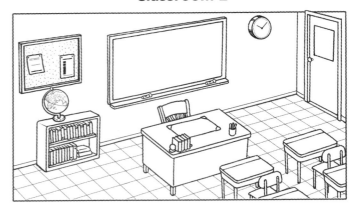

Classroom 1
computer
_____
_____
_____

Classrooms 1 and 2
chairs
_____
_____
_____

Classroom 2
bookcase
_____
_____
_____

B YES OR NO?

Yes 1. There's a computer on the table in Classroom 1.

_____ 2. There's a map on the teacher's desk in Classroom 1.

_____ 3. There's a wastebasket next to the teacher's desk in Classroom 1.

_____ 4. There's a clock next to the bulletin board in Classroom 2.

_____ 5. There's a globe on the bookcase in Classroom 2.

Reaching Out!

Your Classroom

Make a list of everything in your classroom. How is your classroom different from Classroom 1? How is it different from Classroom 2?

8

A WHICH ACTION?

Choose the correct answer.

1. **a.** Stand up.
   b. Sit down.

2. a. Say your name.
   b. Spell your name.

3. a. Go to the board.
   b. Erase the board.

4. a. Print your name.
   b. Sign your name.

5. a. Erase the board.
   b. Write on the board.

6. a. Close your book.
   b. Put away your book.

B WHICH WORD?

Choose the correct word.

1. (**Take**   Raise) your seat.
2. (Say   Read) page ten.
3. (Write on   Take) the board.
4. (Repeat   Open) your book.
5. (Read   Raise) your hand.
6. (Ask   Close) a question.
7. Write on the (name   board).

8. (Put away   Erase) your books.
9. (Go to   Stand) the board.
10. Spell your (name   book).
11. Listen to the (answer   board).
12. (Sit   Stand) down.
13. (Say   Print) your name on the registration form.

Reaching Out!

Work in groups of three. One person is the teacher and gives instructions. Two people are the students and follow the instructions. Take turns as teacher and students. (The teacher can look at the pictures on page 12 of the Basic Picture Dictionary, but *not* the words on page 13.)

Giving & Following Instructions

CLASSROOM ACTIONS II

A WHICH ACTION?

Choose the correct answer.

1. **a.** Work in a group.
   b. Work alone.

2. **a.** Work with a partner.
   b. Correct your mistakes.

3. **a.** Share a book.
   b. Share with the class.

4. **a.** Hand in your homework.
   b. Go over the answers.

5. **a.** Do your own work.
   b. Discuss the question.

6. **a.** Work as a class.
   b. Work with a partner.

B DICTIONARY WORK

Mr. Lorenzo's English class is doing dictionary work. Match his instructions with the pictures.

a

b

__b__ 1. Look in the dictionary.

____ 2. Look up a word.

____ 3. Pronounce the word.

____ 4. Read the definition.

____ 5. Copy the word.

"a mother or father"

c

"parent"

d

`pair-uhnt

e

Reaching Out!

Class Survey

How do students in your class like to work—alone, with a partner, in small groups, or as a class? Take a class survey.

A WHAT'S THE INSTRUCTION?

Maria is Jack's ((sister) brother).
Timmy is Rose's (daughter (son)).

a

father brother husband ~~aunt~~ uncle
pencil marker ~~bookcase~~ chalk pen

b

up / groups. / small / Break / into /
Break up into small groups.

c

r e r l u
ruler

d

My ___address___ is 29 Elm Avenue.
My ___name___ is Donald Peters.

e

place of birth —— 3/29/75
date of birth —— Dallas, Texas

f

The pen is on the ____.
  a. wall
→ b. <u>table</u>
  c. clock

g

My ____ number is 3D.
  a. telephone
  b. social security Ⓐ Ⓑ Ⓒ
  c. apartment

h

__g__ 1. Choose the correct answer.
____ 2. Fill in the blank.
____ 3. Circle the correct answer.
____ 4. Put the words in order.

____ 5. Match the words.
____ 6. Cross out the word.
____ 7. Bubble the answer.
____ 8. Unscramble the word.

B WHICH WORD?

1. Turn on the (shades (lights)).
2. Collect the (tests blanks).
3. (Take out Take) notes.
4. (Turn off Look at) the screen.
5. Bubble the (answers lights).
6. (Pass out Answer) the tests.

7. (Underline Mark) the answer sheet.
8. (Check Collect) your answers.
9. Lower the (notes shades).
10. Answer the (questions answer sheet).
11. (Cross out Take out) a piece of paper.
12. Unscramble the (word test).

Work in groups of three. One person is the teacher. Two people are the students. The teacher is giving a test. The students are following the teacher's instructions. Take turns as teacher and students.

Reaching Out!

Time for a Test

PREPOSITIONS

A A PICTURE

Look at the picture. Circle the correct answers.

1. Rita is (in front of   (next to)) Janet.
2. Janet is (between   to the right of) Rita and Beth.
3. Beth is (behind   in front of) Dennis.
4. Gary is (to the left of   to the right of) Omar.
5. Omar is (between   behind) Janet.
6. Dennis is (to the left of   to the right of) Omar.

Reaching Out!

Your Picture

Draw a picture of your friends, your family, or your classmates. Who are the people in the picture? Write their names on the picture. Where is everyone in the picture? Tell a classmate.

B THE SUPPLY CLOSET

Look at the supply closet. Fill in the missing words.

above	below	between	next to	to the left of	to the right of

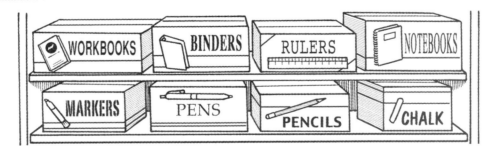

1. The pens are _____ next to _____ the pencils.
2. The rulers are _____ the pencils.
3. The notebooks are _____ the rulers.
4. The binders are _____ the workbooks and the rulers.
5. The markers are _____ the workbooks.
6. The pencils are _____ the chalk.

A WHERE DO THEY WORK?

Match the people with the places at school where they work.

_c_ 1. guidance counselor
____ 2. principal
____ 3. clerk
____ 4. school librarian
____ 5. lunchroom monitor
____ 6. school nurse
____ 7. P.E. teacher
____ 8. science teacher

a. science lab
b. library
c. guidance office
d. gym
e. office
f. cafeteria
g. principal's office
h. nurse's office

B WHO WORKS IN YOUR SCHOOL?

Put a check (✓) next to the people who work in your school.

☐ assistant principal
☐ cafeteria worker
☐ coach
☐ custodian

☐ guidance counselor
☐ P.E. teacher
☐ principal
☐ security officer

☐ school librarian
☐ school nurse
☐ school secretary
☐ science teacher

C THE LAKEVILLE SCHOOL

Look at the diagram of the Lakeville School. Find the rooms in the list below. Write the correct letter next to each room.

_e_ 1. auditorium
____ 2. cafeteria
____ 3. classrooms
____ 4. gym
____ 5. hallway
____ 6. library
____ 7. office
____ 8. track

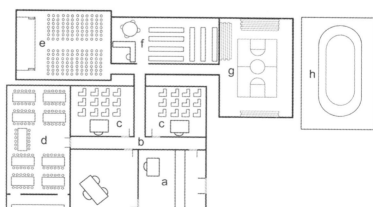

Reaching Out!

What are the rooms in your school? Draw a diagram and label the rooms.

Your School

My School and Classroom

My name is Flora Han. I'm a student at Winslow Elementary School. The school is small. There are five classrooms, a library, a cafeteria, and two offices in the school. The school secretary and the assistant principal work in one office. The other office is the principal's office. There isn't an auditorium in the school, but there's a large gym.

My classroom is next to the principal's office. It's a big classroom with a teacher's desk, a whiteboard, and fifteen desks and chairs for the fifteen students in the class. To the right of my desk, there's a bookcase with many books, workbooks, and dictionaries. Above the bookcase there's a bulletin board. There isn't a computer in the classroom, but there are three computers in the school library.

My teacher, Ms. Lopez, and the teacher's aide, Mr. Martin, are very nice. The students are nice, too. They work together and help each other. I sit next to Marta Rodriguez. When the teacher says, "Break up into small groups" or "Work with a partner," Marta and I work together. I discuss the teacher's questions with Marta.

Ms. Lopez and Mr. Martin say I'm a good student. I study, I take notes, I do my homework, I correct my mistakes, I ask and answer questions, and I look up new words in the dictionary.

1. There are five ____ at Winslow Elementary School.
   a. offices
   b. computers
   c. classrooms

2. Flora's classroom is next to ____.
   a. the school library
   b. the principal's office
   c. the gym

3. Mr. Martin is ____.
   a. a teacher's aide
   b. a teacher
   c. the principal

4. There are ____ in Flora's class.
   a. 5 desks
   b. 19 chairs
   c. 15 students

5. There's a ____ above the bookcase.
   a. whiteboard
   b. bulletin board
   c. clock

6. Flora and ____ are students.
   a. Marta Rodriguez
   b. Ms. Lopez
   c. Mr. Martin

7. There are three computers in ____.
   a. Flora's classroom
   b. the school library
   c. the cafeteria

8. Flora and Marta work together when the teacher says, ____
   a. "Work alone."
   b. "Do your own work."
   c. "Break up into small groups."

A WHAT'S THE ORDER?

Look at page 22 of the Basic Picture Dictionary. Put the actions in order.

Number from 1 to 5.

- [ ] I take a shower.
- [ ] I get dressed.
- [ ] I brush my teeth.
- [1] I get up.
- [ ] I shave.

Number from 1 to 5.

- [ ] I comb my hair.
- [ ] I put on makeup.
- [1] I wash my face.
- [ ] I make the bed.
- [ ] I brush my hair.

Number from 1 to 4.

- [ ] I go to bed.
- [1] I get undressed.
- [ ] I take a bath.
- [ ] I sleep.

B A QUESTIONNAIRE

Answer the questions about yourself. Check (✔) Yes or No. Then work with a partner. Ask your partner the questions. Check (✔) Yes or No.

	You		Your Partner	
	Yes	No	Yes	No
1. Do you eat breakfast every day?				
2. Do you make breakfast?				
3. Do you eat lunch every day?				
4. Do you make lunch?				
5. Do you eat dinner every day?				
6. Do you cook dinner?				

C WHAT DO YOU DO EVERY DAY?

Check (✔) the things you do every day.

- [ ] brush my hair
- [ ] brush my teeth
- [ ] comb my hair
- [ ] cook dinner
- [ ] get dressed
- [ ] get undressed
- [ ] get up
- [ ] go to bed
- [ ] have breakfast
- [ ] have dinner
- [ ] have lunch
- [ ] make breakfast
- [ ] make lunch
- [ ] make the bed
- [ ] put on makeup
- [ ] shave
- [ ] sleep
- [ ] take a bath
- [ ] take a shower
- [ ] wash my face

Make a list of your everyday activities in Exercise C. When do you do each activity? Put the activities in order. Compare with a classmate.

Reaching Out!

Your Everyday Activities

A WHICH WORD?

Carol has many things to do today. Look at her list. Circle the correct words.

THINGS TO DO

1. (Walk **Wash**) the dishes.
2. (Do   Make) the laundry.
3. (Iron   Feed).
4. (Wash   Clean) the apartment.
5. (Go to   Do) the store.
6. Feed the (cat   bus).
7. (Go   Walk) the dog.
8. (Iron   Study) for my test.
9. (Go   Take) to school.

B YOUR DAY

What are you going to do tomorrow? Check (✓) everything you're going to do.

☐ clean the apartment	☐ feed the dog	☐ iron
☐ do the laundry	☐ go to school	☐ study
☐ feed the baby	☐ go to work	☐ walk the dog
☐ feed the cat	☐ go to the store	☐ wash the dishes

C PLAN YOUR DAY

Look at your activities in Exercise B. When are you going to do each activity? Put the activities with a check (✓) in order.

MY DAY

1. _____
2. _____
3. _____
4. _____

5. _____
6. _____
7. _____
8. _____

Reaching Out!

Tomorrow

What are the students in your class going to do tomorrow? How many students are going to clean? How many students are going to do the laundry? Ask about all the activities in Exercise B. Discuss as a class.

A MATCHING

<u>b</u> 1. I'm watching   a. the piano.
____ 2. I'm reading   b. TV.
____ 3. I'm practicing   c. a book.

____ 4. I'm planting   d. to the radio.
____ 5. I'm playing   e. flowers.
____ 6. I'm listening   f. cards.

B SONYA'S FREE TIME

What does Sonya like to do in her free time? Write the activities next to the correct letters.

exercise	play basketball	play the guitar	use the computer
listen to music	play cards	read the newspaper	watch TV

a. __watch TV__   c. _____   e. _____   g. _____
b. _____   d. _____   f. _____   h. _____

C QUESTIONNAIRE

Check (✓) Yes or No.

YOUR LEISURE ACTIVITIES

		Yes	No			Yes	No
1.	Do you like to play cards?	[ ]	[ ]	6.	Do you like to exercise?	[ ]	[ ]
2.	Do you like to watch TV?	[ ]	[ ]	7.	Do you like to swim?	[ ]	[ ]
3.	Do you like to listen to music?	[ ]	[ ]	8.	Do you like to plant flowers?	[ ]	[ ]
4.	Do you like to read?	[ ]	[ ]	9.	Do you like to use a computer?	[ ]	[ ]
5.	Do you like to play basketball?	[ ]	[ ]	10.	Do you like to listen to music?	[ ]	[ ]

> **Reaching Out!**

What do the students in your class like to do? What *don't* they like to do? Take a class survey.

Class Survey

EVERYDAY CONVERSATION 1

A WHAT ARE THEY SAYING?

> Fine, thanks.   Good morning.   Good night.   How are you?   See you later.   What's new?

1.

2.

3.

4.

5.

6.

B WHICH WORD?

> doing   evening   much   new   soon   thanks

1. Fine, _____thanks_____.
2. What's _____ with you?
3. How are you _____?
4. Good _____.
5. See you _____.
6. Not too _____.

> ◄ **Reaching Out!**
>
> *Using Everyday Conversation*
>
> Try to use all the expressions on page 29 of the Basic Picture Dictionary in one day. Make a list of the expressions you use.

A WHAT ARE THEY SAYING?

May I please speak to Mario?   Nice to meet you, too.   Yes. Hold on a moment.
Nice to meet you.   Sorry. I don't understand. You're welcome.

1. Thank you. / You're welcome.

2. Nice to meet you. / ____

3. ____ / I'm sorry. He isn't here right now.

4. This is my husband, Tom. / ____

5. ____

6. May I please speak to Mona? / ____

B WHICH WORD?

1. May I (speak   (ask)) a question?
2. I'd (please   like) to introduce my brother, Paul.
3. Can you please say that (again   repeat)?
4. Hi. (I'm   My name) Robert.
5. (Excuse   Sorry). I don't understand.
6. May I please (speak   introduce) to Karen?
7. Can you please (hold on   repeat) that?

Make a list of all the expressions on page 31 of the Basic Picture Dictionary that you hear in a day. Where do you hear them?

Reaching Out!

Using Everyday Conversation

A WHAT'S THE WEATHER LIKE?

| cloudy | foggy | raining | snowing | sunny | windy |

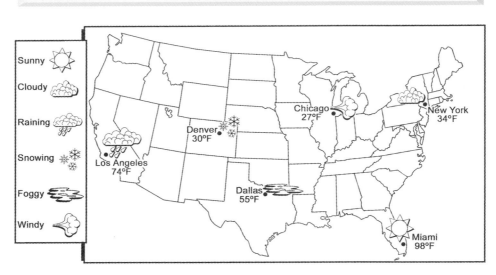

1. It's _____sunny_____ in Miami.
2. It's _____ in New York.
3. It's _____ in Denver.

4. It's _____ in Los Angeles.
5. It's _____ in Chicago.
6. It's _____ in Dallas.

B WHAT'S THE TEMPERATURE?

Look at the map above. What's the temperature in these cities? Is it hot, warm, cool, or cold?

1. It's ___30°___ in Denver. It's _____cold_____.
2. It's _____ in Miami. It's _____.
3. It's _____ in Dallas. It's _____.
4. It's _____ in Los Angeles. It's _____.

C WHICH CITY?

Look at the map above. Choose the correct answer.

1. It's raining in ((Los Angeles)   Dallas).
2. It's foggy in (Dallas   New York).
3. It's cloudy in (Miami   New York).
4. There's a snowstorm in (Denver   Chicago).
5. There's a heat wave in (New York   Miami).

Reaching Out!

Five Cities

Watch a weather forecast on TV or look in the newspaper. What's the weather in five different cities today? What's the weather forecast for tomorrow?

A Day with Claudia and Alex

I'm Claudia Ruiz. I'm a teacher's aide at the Carroll School in Los Angeles. Every morning I get up, I take a shower, I get dressed, and I eat breakfast. Then I make lunch and I drive to school. I eat my lunch at school.

My husband, Alex, is at home every morning. He gets up, he makes breakfast, and he feeds the baby. Then he washes the dishes, makes the bed, and does the laundry. When the baby is sleeping, he reads the newspaper and uses the computer.

At the Carroll School, I help the teacher and the students. When I come home from school, Alex goes to work.

Every afternoon I clean the apartment and I go to the store. When it's warm and sunny, I plant flowers. When it's raining, I iron and I write letters to my sister and brother in Mexico. Every evening I feed the baby, I cook, and I have dinner alone. Then the baby goes to bed and I relax. I listen to music and I read.

When Alex comes home from work, he eats dinner. Then I wash the dishes, and Alex and I watch TV together.

1. Every morning Claudia ____.
   a. eats lunch
   b. makes the bed
   c. gets dressed
   d. washes the dishes

2. At the Carroll School, Claudia ____.
   a. feeds the baby
   b. helps the teacher and the students
   c. eats breakfast
   d. writes letters

3. Every afternoon Claudia ____.
   a. takes a shower
   b. reads the newspaper
   c. drives to work
   d. goes to the store

4. Every evening Claudia ____.
   a. irons
   b. comes home from work
   c. cooks dinner
   d. writes letters

5. Claudia makes lunch ____.
   a. every morning
   b. every afternoon
   c. every evening
   d. when it's raining

6. Claudia plants flowers when ____.
   a. it's raining
   b. it's cloudy
   c. it's hailing
   d. it's sunny

7. Alex ____.
   a. is a teacher's aide
   b. does the laundry
   c. listens to music every evening
   d. cleans the apartment

8. Alex and Claudia ____ together.
   a. eat dinner
   b. clean the apartment
   c. read the newspaper
   d. watch TV

A WHAT'S THE NUMBER?

Fill in the missing numbers and number words.

5	five
	nine
3	
	fourteen
12	

	twenty
22	
	sixty-four
79	
	eighty-six

93	
	one hundred
112	
	one thousand
10,000	

B AN IDENTIFICATION CARD

IDENTIFICATION CARD

Name: Orlando Valdez
Address: 1359 Elm Street, Apt. #317
Dallas, TX 75392
Telephone Number: (214) 574-9628
Social Security Number: 253-19-5287
Date of Birth: 7/15/89

_c_ 1. My address is
____ 2. My social security number is
____ 3. My date of birth is
____ 4. My apartment number is
____ 5. My zip code is
____ 6. My telephone number is

a. seven / fifteen / eighty-nine.
b. three seventeen.
c. thirteen fifty-nine Elm Street.
d. two one four - five seven four - nine six two eight.
e. two five three - one nine - five two eight seven.
f. seven five three nine two.

C COMPLETE THE CLASSROOM INVENTORY

Item	Number of Items
bookcases	3
books	
calculators	
chairs	
desks	
markers	
notebooks	

1. There are three bookcases.
2. There are one hundred fifty books.
3. There are seventeen calculators.
4. There are forty-one chairs.
5. There are thirty-nine desks.
6. There are eleven markers.
7. There are twenty-eight notebooks.

Reaching Out!

Classroom Inventory

Take an inventory of your classroom. How many bookcases, books, calculators, chairs, desks, markers, and notebooks are there in your classroom?

ORDINAL NUMBERS

BASIC DICTIONARY
PAGE 35

A WHAT'S THE NUMBER?

Fill in the missing numbers and number words.

1st	first
	third
7th	

	twelfth
21st	
	fortieth

62nd	
	eighty-fifth
100th	

B WHICH FLOOR?

Midtown Medical Building

Name	Floor	Name	Floor
Gordon Andrews, MD	9	Edward Kaye, MD	3
Jean Carroll, MD	1	Lois McDonald, MD	11
Mario Diego, MD	5	Mark Peters, MD	8
Elizabeth Gomez, MD	14	Lydia Santini, MD	2

  b 1. Dr. Andrews is on the
____ 2. Dr. Carroll is on the
____ 3. Dr. Diego is on the
____ 4. Dr. Gomez is on the
____ 5. Dr. Kaye is on the
____ 6. Dr. McDonald is on the
____ 7. Dr. Peters is on the
____ 8. Dr. Santini is on the

a. third floor.
b. ninth floor.
c. eleventh floor.
d. second floor.
e. fifth floor.
f. eighth floor.
g. first floor.
h. fourteenth floor.

C WHAT'S THE STREET?

Look at the address book. Write the name of the street with numbers.

Name	Address
Beth Abbott	203 Sixth Avenue
Donald Abrams	26 Seventy-eighth Street
Rose Allen	753 Ninety-first Street
Marjorie Alvarez	125 Forty-third Street
Ralph Ames	1390 One hundred tenth Street
Mona Arnold	376 Second Avenue

1. 203 __6th__ Avenue
2. 26 _____ Street
3. 753 _____ Street
4. 125 _____ Street
5. 1390 _____ Street
6. 376 _____ Avenue

Reaching Out!

What are some streets in your city or town with number names?
Make a list. Compare with a classmate.

Streets with Number Names

A WHAT'S THE TIME?

Complete the clocks.

1. five o'clock
2. one fifteen
3. six twenty
4. ten thirty

7:45

5. seven forty-five
6. nine fifty-five
7. two oh five
8. ten to eight

B WHICH TIME IS CORRECT?

Choose the correct time.

9:30

1. a. It's nine thirty.
   b. It's nine thirteen.

2. a. It's ten to three.
   b. It's ten after three.

10:45

3. a. It's a quarter to eleven.
   b. It's a quarter after ten.

4. a. It's midnight.
   b. It's noon.

6:05

5. a. It's six oh five.
   b. It's five to six.

6. a. It's two A.M.
   b. It's two P.M.

C MATCH THE TIMES

Look at the train schedule and match the times.

City	Train 1	Train 2
Acton	6:10	7:10
Easton	6:15	7:15
Richmond	6:30	7:30
Oakdale	6:45	7:45
Fairview	6:55	7:55

1. Train 1 leaves Acton at
2. Train 1 leaves Richmond at
3. Train 1 leaves Fairview at
4. Train 2 leaves Acton at
5. Train 2 leaves Easton at
6. Train 2 leaves Oakdale at

ten after seven.
five to seven.
a quarter after seven.
six ten.
seven forty-five.
half past six.

Reaching Out!

Every Day

Write about times in your everyday life. For example: I get up at six o'clock. I go to school/work at . . . Then share your information with a classmate.

A HOW MUCH IS IT?

1. __50¢__ or __$.50__

2. _____ or _____

3. _____ or _____

4. _____ or _____

5. _____ or _____

6. _____

B MATCHING: *COINS AND AMOUNTS*

1.	silver dollar	fifty cents	5¢
2.	penny	one cent	$1.00
3.	half dollar	five cents	$.01
4.	quarter	one dollar	10¢
5.	nickel	ten cents	$.25
6.	dime	twenty-five cents	$.50

C WHAT'S THE AMOUNT?

$.16	$.25	$.30	$.51	$.60	$.75

1.

_____ $.25 _____

2.

_____

3.

_____

4.

_____

5.

_____

6.

_____

Reaching Out!

What coins do you have with you today? How much is each coin worth? How much are they worth all together?

Your Coins

A WHAT'S THE AMOUNT?

1. _____$6.00_____

2. _____

3. _____

4. _____

5. _____

6. _____

B HOW MUCH IS IT?

1. four one-dollar bills ___$4.00___
2. two five-dollar bills _____
3. five ten-dollar bills _____
4. three twenty-dollar bills _____

5. a ten-dollar bill and a quarter _____
6. a one-dollar bill and a nickel _____
7. a twenty-dollar bill and two dimes _____
8. a five-dollar bill and three pennies _____

C BACK-TO-SCHOOL SALE

Write the prices on the coupons.

1. A pen costs two dollars and ninety-nine cents.
2. A ruler costs four dollars and thirty cents.
3. A monitor costs seven hundred dollars.
4. A printer costs one hundred twenty-five dollars.
5. A calculator costs fifteen dollars and ninety cents.
6. A spiral notebook costs a dollar seventy-five.

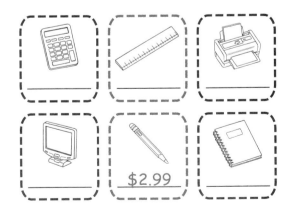

$2.99

Reaching Out!

How Much?

Go to a store and look for the items in Exercise C. How much do they cost?

A WHICH DAY?

Look at the calendar on page 40 of the Basic Picture Dictionary. Complete the sentences.

1. January 5, 2012 is on a ___Thursday___.
2. January 9, 2012 is on a _____.
3. January 18, 2012 is on a _____.

4. January 24, 2012 is on a _____.
5. January 29, 2012 is on a _____.
6. January 13, 2012 is on a _____.

B MONTHS OF THE YEAR

Complete the chart.

Month	Abbreviation
October	OCT
	DEC
January	
	APR

Month	Abbreviation
February	
	MAY
July	
	SEP

Month	Abbreviation
November	
	MAR
August	
	JUN

C DATES

Complete the chart.

Month/Day/Year	Month/Day/Year
January 25, 2009	1/25/2009
	2/18/2009
April 13, 2009	
	6/22/2010

Month/Day/Year	Month/Day/Year
July 14, 2010	
	9/5/2010
October 20, 2011	
	12/31/2012

D TODAY

Write about today.

1. The year is _____.
2. The month is _____.

3. The day of the week is _____.
4. Today's date is _____.

E U.S. HOLIDAYS

Look at a calendar for this year. Write the date of the holidays.

1. New Year's Day is on ___January 1___.
2. Presidents Day is on _____.
3. Memorial Day is on _____.

4. Independence Day is on _____.
5. Halloween is on _____.
6. Veterans Day is on _____.

Reaching Out!

Interview your classmates. When are their birthdays? Make a list of birthdays in the class.

Birthdays

TIME EXPRESSIONS AND SEASONS

BASIC DICTIONARY PAGES 42–43

A WHAT'S THE ORDER?

Number the time expressions from 1 to 6.

	tomorrow morning		tonight		last night
1	yesterday morning		this afternoon		tomorrow evening

B WHEN IS IT?

Today is Wednesday, January 11. Match the times and dates with the time expressions.

TUE	WED	THU
10	(11)	12

__b__ 1. January 11, 8:00 A.M.   a. yesterday evening

____ 2. January 12, 1:00 P.M.   b. this morning

____ 3. January 11, 9:00 P.M.   c. tomorrow afternoon

____ 4. January 10, 7:00 P.M.   d. tonight

C SEASONS

Match the months and seasons.

February   Summer   May

October   Spring   January

July   Winter   November

April   Fall   August

D NINA'S CALENDAR

Look at Nina's calendar. Circle the correct answers.

Sunday	Monday	Tuesday	Wednesday	Thursday	Friday	Saturday
1	2	3	4	5	6	7
do the laundry iron wash the dishes	go to school wash the dishes	go to work wash the dishes	go to school go to the store wash the dishes	go to school wash the dishes	go to work go to the store wash the dishes	clean the apartment wash the dishes

1. She irons ((once a week)   twice a week).
2. She washes the dishes (three times a week   every day).
3. She goes to work (twice a week   three times a week).
4. She cleans the apartment (once a week   twice a week).
5. She goes to school (twice a week   three times a week).
6. She (goes to the store   does the laundry) once a week.

Reaching Out!

Every Week

What activities do you do every week? How many times a week do you do them? Compare with a classmate.

A Letter to Parents

Dear Parents,

School is going to begin very soon. Here is the schedule for the new school year. Wednesday, September 3rd is the first day of school for all students in grades 2 to 5. The first day of school for all first-grade students is Thursday, September 4th. The school day is from 8:15 A.M. to 2:15 P.M. There is also an after-school program for children from 2:30 P.M. to 5:00 P.M.

Students have a half day of school on Tuesday, September 16th. There are four other half days this year—Wednesday, November 26th, Tuesday, February 3rd, Friday, March 20th, and Monday, May 4th. On half days, students leave school at 11:30 A.M., and the after-school program begins at 11:45 A.M.

Wednesday, October 22nd is Open School Day. Come to school in the morning or afternoon and meet your child's teacher. Winter holidays are from December 24th to January 2nd. Classes begin again on Monday, January 4th. Spring holidays are the second week in April—from April 6th to April 10th. Finally, the last day of school this year is on Friday, June 5th.

Call the school with any questions about your child's schedule.

Sincerely,

Lena Markova

Lena Markova, Principal

1. The first day of school for students in the fourth grade is on ____.
   a. September first
   b. September second
   c. September third
   d. September fourth

2. School begins at ____.
   a. a quarter to eight
   b. a quarter after eight
   c. half past eight
   d. eight fifty

3. ____ is a half day.
   a. September fifteenth
   b. November twenty-seventh
   c. February fourth
   d. March twentieth

4. Open School Day is on a ____.
   a. Monday
   b. Tuesday
   c. Wednesday
   d. Thursday

5. Spring holidays are ____ in April.
   a. the 1st week in April
   b. the 2nd week in April
   c. the 3rd week in April
   d. the last week in April

6. There is no school on ____.
   a. December twenty-seventh
   b. January fourth
   c. April eleventh
   d. June fifth

A AMY'S TAXI

Amy drives a taxi. Look at the pictures. Where did she go today?

apartment building	dormitory	duplex	farm	houseboat	townhouse

9:00 A.M.

10:15 A.M.

11:00 A.M.

12:45 P.M.

2:10 P.M.

3:30 P.M.

9:00 A.M.	townhouse
10:15 A.M.	_____
11:00 A.M.	_____
12:45 P.M.	_____
2:10 P.M.	_____
3:30 P.M.	_____

B WHAT IS IT?

city	dormitory	duplex	mobile home	nursing home	ranch	shelter

1. A _____duplex_____ is a house for two families.
2. A _____ is a building for old people.
3. A _____ is a building for students.
4. A _____ is a building for people with no place to live.
5. A _____ is a large town.
6. A _____ is a large farm with animals.
7. A _____ is a house you can drive.

C PEOPLE I KNOW

Complete the sentences with the names of people you know.

1. .... lives in a house.
2. .... lives in an apartment.
3. .... lives in a duplex.
4. .... lives in a townhouse.
5. .... lives in a dormitory.
6. .... lives in the suburbs.

◀ **Reaching Out!**

Where We Live

Interview three classmates. Ask: Where do you live? What type of housing and community is it? Then write sentences about them.

THE LIVING ROOM

A WHAT'S THE WORD?

Look at the picture on page 46 of the Basic Picture Dictionary. Write the correct words.

coffee table	end table	loveseat	mantel	pillow	sofa	VCR

1. The woman is sitting on the _____ sofa _____.
2. There's a window behind the _____.
3. There's a painting above the _____.
4. There's a book on the _____.
5. There's a _____ on the couch.
6. There's a lamp on the _____.
7. There's a _____ on the TV.

B CROSS OUT ONE

Look at page 46 of the Basic Picture Dictionary. Cross out the item that doesn't belong.

1. **On the wall:** painting photograph ~~fireplace screen~~
2. **In the wall unit:** speaker DVD player stereo system
3. **On the floor:** drapes rug loveseat
4. **On a table:** lamp magazine holder plant
5. **To the right of the armchair:** floor lamp end table fireplace

C GOING SHOPPING!

Read the store directory. Check (✓) the floor where you can find each of the following items.

	1st Floor	2nd Floor	3rd Floor	4th Floor
1.			✓	
2.				
3.				
4.				
5.				

House & Home Store

Floor	
1	Couches, Loveseats, Armchairs
2	Lamps, Floor Lamps, Plants
3	Wall Units, Bookcases, End Tables
4	Televisions, DVD Players, Stereo Systems

Reaching Out!

Go to a furniture store or a department store. Find five living room items. What are they? How much do they cost?

Find Five Items

A IN THE DINING ROOM

Look at the picture on page 48 of the Basic Picture Dictionary. Circle the correct answers.

1. The candle is in the ((candlestick) vase).
2. The knife is to the left of the (spoon   fork).
3. The coffee pot is on the (table   tray).
4. The (butter dish   pitcher) is on the table.
5. The (sugar bowl   pepper shaker) is on the buffet.
6. The (plate   platter) is between the fork and the knife.
7. The (cup   mug) is on the saucer.
8. The (serving dish   tablecloth) is under the serving bowl.

B THE YARD SALE

You're at the Millers' yard sale. Check the items on your list that the Millers are selling today.

To Buy

✓	china cabinet
___	buffet
___	dining room chairs
___	chandelier
___	teapot
___	coffee pot
___	serving dish
___	pitcher
___	sugar bowl
___	mugs
___	glasses
___	butter dish
___	salt shaker
___	napkins

C HOW MUCH IS IT?

glass	$1.00	napkin	
	$7.00		$40.00
	$1.50	pitcher	
china cabinet			$5.00
	50¢	mug	

> **Reaching Out!**
>
> *Yard Sale*
>
> You're going to have a yard sale! Make a list of five dining room items you want to sell and a price for each. Ask a classmate if each item is a good price.

A WHERE ARE THEY?

Look at the picture on page 50 of the Basic Picture Dictionary. Check where you see the items.

	On the Nightstand	On the Dresser	On the Bed	On the Window
blinds				✓
pillow				
alarm clock				
jewelry box				
curtains				
sheet				
clock radio				
blanket				
quilt				

B TWO BEDROOMS

Look at these two bedrooms. Write the items you see in the correct places below.

bed frame	blinds	carpet	dresser	lamp	mirror
blanket	box spring	curtains	headboard	mattress	nightstand

Bedroom 1

Bedroom 2

Bedroom 1
bed frame
_____
_____
_____

Bedrooms 1 & 2
_____
_____
_____
_____

Bedroom 2
_____
_____
_____
_____

Reaching Out!

On a separate sheet of paper, draw a picture of your bedroom and write sentences to describe it. Compare with a classmate.

My Bedroom

A WHERE IN THE KITCHEN?

Look at the kitchen on page 52 of the Basic Picture Dictionary. Find the following items.
Then write each word in the correct column.

| cabinet | cookbook | dish rack | food processor | placemat | spice rack |
| canister | cutting board | dishwasher detergent | microwave | potholder | toaster oven |

Counter	Wall	Kitchen Table
canister		

B A KITCHEN SALE

Look at the advertisement and fill in the chart.

The Kitchen Store

$32 $19 $10 $13 $35
$50 $17 $20 $2 $3

tea kettle	$10
	$17
toaster	
	$3
electric mixer	
	$20
dishwashing liquid	
	$19
electric can opener	
	$35

C IN MY KITCHEN

What do you have in your kitchen? Check (✓) the items you have on the following list.

- ☐ freezer
- ☐ stove
- ☐ kitchen sink
- ☐ dishwasher
- ☐ garbage disposal
- ☐ burners
- ☐ paper towel holder
- ☐ oven
- ☐ food processor
- ☐ faucet
- ☐ refrigerator
- ☐ microwave

Reaching Out!

Kitchen Items

What are your ten favorite kitchen items? Make a list.
Then compare lists with a classmate.

THE BABY'S ROOM

A BABY GIFTS

Paula is going to have a baby. Her friends had a "baby shower" party for her and gave her gifts.

From Claudia
From Rita
From Kathy
From Janet
From Gloria
From Flora

Paula is making a list of all the gifts. What did each friend give her? Complete the list.

baby carriage
car seat
cradle
high chair
mobile
stroller

My Gifts

Rita _____car seat_____   Gloria _____

Kathy _____   Flora _____

Janet _____   Claudia _____

B A THANK-YOU NOTE

Look at Paula's thank-you note to Claudia.

Dear Claudia,

    Thank you for the beautiful stroller. It's a wonderful gift.

            Sincerely,
            Paula

Write a thank-you note from Paula to a different friend.

C BABIES IN YOUR COUNTRY

What do people use for babies in your country? Check (✓) the items below.

- [ ] baby backpack
- [ ] baby monitor
- [ ] car seat
- [ ] cradle
- [ ] crib bumper
- [ ] diaper pail
- [ ] food warmer
- [ ] mobile
- [ ] night light
- [ ] playpen
- [ ] potty
- [ ] stroller
- [ ] swing
- [ ] toy chest
- [ ] walker

Make a list of ten important things to buy for a baby. Then compare lists with a classmate.

Reaching Out!

What to Buy

BASIC DICTIONARY
PAGES 56–57

A WHERE ARE THEY?

*Look at the picture on page 56 of the Basic Picture Dictionary. Find the following items.
Then write each word in the correct column.*

bath mat	hair dryer	plunger	soap dish	toilet brush
bathtub	hamper	scale	soap dispenser	towel rack
electric toothbrush	medicine cabinet	shelf	toilet	wastebasket

On the Wall	On the Floor	On the Vanity
medicine cabinet		

B WHAT IS IT?

__h__ 1. You brush your teeth with ____.

____ 2. You wash your face with ____.

____ 3. You dry your hands and face with ____.

____ 4. You dry your hair with ____.

____ 5. You fix the toilet with ____.

____ 6. You clean the bathtub and sink with ____.

____ 7. You stand in the bathtub on ____.

____ 8. You put dirty clothes in ____.

____ 9. You turn on the water with ____.

a. a hand towel

b. a plunger

c. a sponge

d. a faucet

e. a hamper

f. a washcloth

g. a hair dryer

h. a toothbrush

i. a rubber mat

C HOW MUCH IS IT?

Write the prices on the coupons.

1. A sponge costs two dollars and ninety-nine cents.
2. A toothbrush costs a dollar seventy-five.
3. A scale costs twenty-three fifty.
4. A hair dryer costs thirteen ninety-nine.
5. Air freshener costs three forty-nine.
6. A soap dish costs a dollar twenty-two.

$2.99

Reaching Out!

Your Bathroom

Draw a picture of your bathroom. What's in it? Where is everything?
Compare pictures with a classmate and talk about them.

OUTSIDE THE HOME

A REPAIR TIME!

Check the six things that someone needs to repair.

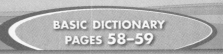

☐ back door	☐ drainpipe	☐ gutter	☐ patio	☐ side door
☑ deck	☐ fence	☐ lawn chair	☐ screen door	☐ tool shed

B WHICH HOUSE IS FOR SALE?

Read the following advertisement. Look at the houses below and put a check under the house that's in the ad.

76 Sunset Drive, Raymond, California $550,000
                                                          4 Bedrooms, 2 Bathrooms

This beautiful house has a large front porch, a 2-car garage, new shutters, and a satellite dish. It's near schools and shopping.

____   ____   ____

C YOUR AD FOR A HOUSE

Write your own advertisement for a house.

$ ....

....
(address)

.... Bedrooms, ... Bathrooms

This beautiful house has ....

It's near ....

Reaching Out!

Draw a picture of a beautiful house for you and your family. Write about it. Share with a classmate.

A Beautiful House

A A NEW APARTMENT

Carlos is looking for a new apartment. Number the following 1–8 in the correct order.

☐ Give a security deposit. ☐ Sign a lease. ☐ Move into the apartment.

☐ Look at the apartment. ☐ Rent a moving truck. ☐ See an apartment ad.

1 Buy a newspaper. ☐ Call the building manager.

B PEOPLE AND BUILDINGS

Put each word into the correct group.

balcony	building manager
landlord	fire escape
roof	tenant

People	Parts of a Building
landlord	

C APARTMENT ADS

BELLTOWN 2 bedrooms, dining room, large kitchen, balcony, 4th floor. $900. No security deposit. Call landlord 909-356-9872.

BLOOMINGTON 3 bedrooms, 2 bathrooms, parking garage, 2nd floor. Doorman in building. $1000. Call building manager 909-289-2589.

CANYON LAKE 1 bedroom with air conditioner, 3rd floor. Swimming pool & whirlpool in courtyard. $850. Call building manager 909-875-0964.

1. The apartment in Canyon Lake has ____.
   a. two bedrooms
   b. an air conditioner *(circled)*
   c. a balcony

2. The apartment building in Bloomington has ____.
   a. a courtyard
   b. a whirlpool
   c. a parking garage

3. You don't pay a security deposit for the apartment in ____.
   a. Belltown
   b. Bloomington
   c. Canyon Lake

4. The apartment in Belltown ____.
   a. is on the second floor
   b. has a balcony
   c. has two bathrooms

5. The apartment building in ____ has a swimming pool.
   a. Belltown
   b. Bloomington
   c. Canyon Lake

6. To see the apartment in Bloomington, call the ____.
   a. doorman
   b. building manager
   c. landlord

Reaching Out!

Write an Ad

Write an ad for an apartment. In groups of four, read your ads. Which apartment is your group going to rent? Why?

THE APARTMENT BUILDING II

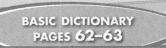

A WHERE ARE THEY?

Look at page 62 of the Basic Picture Dictionary. Check where you see the items.

	In the Lobby	In the Hallway	In the Basement	On the Door
fire alarm		✓		
garbage chute				
intercom				
laundry room				
mailboxes				
peephole				
storage locker				

B WHICH GROUP?

buzzer	fire alarm	lock	security gate	sprinkler system
door chain	intercom	peephole	smoke detector	

For Fire Safety	For Security		
fire alarm	buzzer		

C APARTMENT ADS

Read the apartment ads. Decide if the following sentences are True (T) or False (F).

BALLARD 2 bedrooms, new kitchen with dishwasher, 3rd floor. Elevator in building. $850. Call building manager 805-379-1483.

CRESTON 1 bedroom apartment on 2nd floor. Safe building with intercom, security gate, and sprinkler system. $750. Call landlord 805-224-2530.

FILLMORE 1 bedroom, large kitchen, 4th floor. Laundry room and storage lockers in basement. $700. Call superintendent 805-627-0045.

_T_ 1. The apartment building in Fillmore has a laundry room.

____ 2. Call the superintendent to see the apartment in Ballard.

____ 3. The apartment building in Creston has a sprinkler system.

____ 4. The apartment on the fourth floor has one bedroom.

____ 5. The two-bedroom apartment has a balcony.

____ 6. The apartment in Fillmore is in the basement.

Reaching Out!

What safety and security items are there in your home? Make a list. Compare with a classmate.

A Safe Apartment

A) THIS HOUSE HAS PROBLEMS!

This house has a lot of problems! Check (✓) the problems you see.

- ✓ The roof is leaking.
- ☐ There are mice.
- ☐ A sink is clogged.
- ☐ There are ants.
- ☐ A wall is cracked.
- ☐ The toilet is broken.
- ☐ There are cockroaches.
- ☐ The refrigerator is broken.
- ☐ The hot water heater isn't working.

B) WHO CAN FIX IT?

Match the housing problem with the person who fixes it.

_c_	1. The bathtub is leaking.	a.	the exterminator
____	2. The wall is cracked.	b.	the appliance repairperson
____	3. The roof is leaking.	c.	the plumber
____	4. The stove isn't working.	d.	the house painter
____	5. There are termites in the kitchen.	e.	the roofer

C) REPAIRS

exterminator	leaking	peeling	sink	termites	working

REPAIR REQUEST FORM

NAME: _José Diaz_

ADDRESS: _1528 Center Avenue #20A_

PROBLEM/WORK REQUIRED: The bathtub is _____leaking_____[1], the paint in the bedroom is _____[2], the refrigerator isn't _____[3], and the kitchen _____[4] is clogged. Call the _____[5]. There are cockroaches and _____[6] in the apartment.

◄ **Reaching Out!**

Who Do You Call?

Who do you call when you have the problems in this lesson? Make a list of the people you call. Share your list with the class.

A WHAT'S THE WORD?

Look at the household problems on page 66 of the Basic Picture Dictionary. Complete the sentences.

| chimneysweep | door | doorbell | electrician | power | steps | tiles |

1. The _____door_____ doesn't open.
2. The _____ is fixing the front light.
3. The carpenter is fixing the _____. They're broken.
4. The _____ doesn't ring.
5. The _____ in the bathroom are loose.
6. The _____ is standing on the roof.
7. The _____ is out in the living room.

B WHO CAN FIX IT?

Match the housing problem with the person who fixes it.

_c_ 1. The lock is broken.   a. the chimneysweep
____ 2. The power is out.   b. the carpenter
____ 3. The chimney is dirty.   c. the locksmith
____ 4. The steps are broken.   d. the home repairperson
____ 5. The tiles in the bathroom are loose.   e. the electrician

C LOOK IN THE YELLOW PAGES!

1. My chimney is dirty.   Call __305-478-1129__.
2. My air conditioning isn't working.   Call _____.
3. My front light doesn't go on.   Call _____.
4. My side door doesn't open.   Call _____.
5. The lock on my front door is broken.   Call _____.
6. My doorbell doesn't ring.   Call _____.

Who do you call when you have the problems in this lesson?
Make a list of the people you call. Share your list with the class.

Reaching Out!

Repairpeople

41

A MATCHING SUPPLIES

_c_ 1. You sweep the floor with a broom and ____.

____ 2. You mop the floor with a mop and ____.

____ 3. You wash the windows with window cleaner and ____.

____ 4. You vacuum with a vacuum and vacuum cleaner ____.

____ 5. You clean the toilet with cleanser and ____.

a. a scrub brush
b. paper towels
c. a dust pan
d. a bucket
e. attachments

B YOUR CLEANING SUPPLIES

Check the cleaning supplies you have in your home right now. Then make a shopping list of the cleaning supplies you need to buy.

☐ ammonia
☐ cleanser
☐ sponges
☐ window cleaner
☐ vacuum cleaner bags

☐ furniture polish
☐ floor wax
☐ scrub brush
☐ paper towels
☐ dust cloth

Cleaning Supplies to Buy

_____
_____
_____
_____
_____

C FOUR FRIENDS

Maria, Susan, Vera, and Karen live together. Every week they clean together, but they have different chores. Look at the chart and decide if the sentences are True or False.

1. Susan is going to mop the floor on May 21st.

   (True)   False

2. Maria is going to sweep the floor on May 7th.

   True   False

3. Susan is going to vacuum on May 14th.

   True   False

4. Vera is going to dust on May 21st.

   True   False

5. Karen is going to vacuum on May 14th.

   True   False

6. Vera is going to mop the floor on May 7th.

   True   False

CHORES	May 7	May 14	May 21
(vacuum)	Maria	Susan	Karen
(mop and bucket)	Vera	Karen	Susan
(duster)	Karen	Maria	Vera
(broom)	Susan	Vera	Maria

Reaching Out!

Household Chores

Who does each household cleaning chore in your home? When? Share with a classmate.

A JANE'S TOOLBOX

Jane is cleaning her toolbox. Check (✓) each item she has and tell how many.

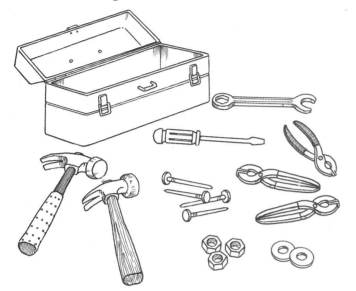

Tools/Hardware	✓	How Many?
bolt		
hammer	✓	2
nail		
nut		
pliers		
saw		
screw		
screwdriver		
washer		
wrench		

B YOUR TOOLBOX

Do you have any tools? Check the ones you have.

- ☐ electric drill
- ☐ hammer
- ☐ monkey wrench
- ☐ pliers
- ☐ saw
- ☐ screwdriver
- ☐ vise
- ☐ wrench

C HOW MUCH IS IT?

Harry's Hardware Store
This Week's Specials!

$2.87 $7.99 $2.49
$9.97 $45.00 $15.80
$2.98 $32.94

Look at the items on sale at Harry's Hardware Store. Complete the sentences.

1. The flashlights cost ___$7.99___.
2. The wheelbarrows cost _____.
3. The yardsticks cost _____.
4. The rakes cost _____.
5. The ladders cost _____.
6. The batteries cost _____.
7. The shovels cost _____.
8. The lightbulbs cost _____.

Reaching Out!

When did you fix something in your home? What was the problem?
What tools and supplies did you use? Share with a classmate.

Tools and Repairs

Mandy and Pablo's Apartment

Mandy and Pablo Gomez live in an apartment on the fourth floor of a large apartment building in Riverdale. Their apartment has a small kitchen, a large living room, a large bedroom, and a bathroom.

Mandy and Pablo take good care of their apartment. Mandy vacuums the living room and bedroom carpets and dusts the furniture. She also polishes the coffee table and the wall unit in the living room and the dressers and night tables in the bedroom. Pablo mops and waxes the kitchen floor and cleans the kitchen counters and cabinets. He also mops the bathroom floor and uses a scrub brush, cleanser, and a sponge to clean the bathtub, shower, and toilet.

But Mandy and Pablo's apartment is old, and it has many problems. The paint in the living room is peeling, the tiles in the bathroom are loose, the stove isn't working, and the doorbell doesn't ring. Also, the elevator in the apartment building isn't working, so Mandy and Pablo use the stairway to get to the fourth floor.

Mandy and Pablo call the superintendent every week, but he doesn't fix anything. They think it's time to find a new apartment. They're looking at this apartment ad in the newspaper. They're going to make an appointment to see it.

> **RIVERDALE** 1-bedroom apartment on 2nd floor. New kitchen with dishwasher. Laundry room and storage lockers in basement. Elevator in building. 2-year lease. No security deposit. $850. Call landlord 708-561-2798

1. Mandy and Pablo's apartment has ____.
   a. a large kitchen
   b. a small living room
   c. a large bedroom
   d. a balcony

2. Mandy cleans ____.
   a. the kitchen counters
   b. the bathroom floor
   c. the bathtub
   d. the furniture

3. Pablo does NOT use ____ when he cleans.
   a. a scrub brush
   b. a sponge
   c. a vacuum
   d. floor wax

4. Mandy and Pablo's ____ isn't working.
   a. toilet
   b. doorbell
   c. sink
   d. cable TV

5. Mandy and Pablo are looking for a new apartment because ____.
   a. their apartment is small
   b. their apartment is in Riverdale
   c. their apartment is dirty
   d. the superintendent doesn't fix things

6. The apartment in the ad ____.
   a. has a dishwasher
   b. has two bedrooms
   c. is on the fourth floor
   d. has a broken lock

A SHOPPING IN CENTERVILLE

| Sunshine Coffee Shop | | West Street Clinic | | Day & Night Convenience Store | Little Friends Day-Care Center | | Centerville Bus Station |

| | Tech World Computer Store | City Bank | | Henry's Barber Shop | | Harper's Book Store |

Look at the map of downtown Centerville. Where can you do the following things?

1. get some money? _____City Bank_____
2. have breakfast? _____
3. see a doctor? _____
4. buy a monitor or a keyboard? _____
5. buy an English dictionary? _____
6. take your child when you're at work? _____
7. get a haircut? _____
8. get the bus to New York? _____
9. buy dishwashing liquid? _____

B PLACES YOU LIKE

What stores and other places in your community do you like? Choose five places from the list and complete the chart.

bakery	book store	clinic	computer store
bank	child-care center	clothing store	convenience store
barber shop	cleaners	coffee shop	

Type of Place	Name of the Place You Like
bakery	Rosa's Bakery

Reaching Out!

Where Did You Go?

Which of the places on this page did you go to this month? What did you do there? Share with a classmate.

PLACES AROUND TOWN II

A WHAT'S THE PLACE?

```
                           NORTH STREET
S                                                                      S
I                                                                      E
X    DRUG      FURNITURE    SERVICE      DEPARTMENT        HAIR        V
T    STORE       STORE      STATION        STORE          SALON        E
H                                                                      N
                                                                       T
S                                                           GROCERY    H
T    FLORIST   FAST-FOOD               ELECTRONICS          STORE      S
R              RESTAURANT                 STORE                        T
E                                                                      R
E                                                                      E
T                                                                      E
                        WASHINGTON STREET                             T
```

1. You can get a haircut at the _____hair salon_____ on Seventh Street.
2. You can have lunch at the _____ on Washington Street.
3. You can buy an armchair or a sofa at the _____ on Sixth Street.
4. You can buy a DVD player at the _____ on Washington Street.
5. You can buy potholders and dishes at the _____ on North Street.
6. You can buy flowers at the _____ on Washington Street.
7. You can get gas for your car at the _____ on _____ Street.
8. You can buy milk and bread at the _____ on _____ Street.
9. You can buy medicine at the _____ on _____ Street.

B PLACES YOU LIKE

What stores and other places in your community do you like? Choose five places from the list and complete the chart.

department store	drug store	fast-food restaurant	gas station
discount store	electronics store	flower shop	grocery store
donut shop	eye-care center	furniture store	hair salon

Type of Place	Name of the Place You Like
department store	Wilson's Department Store

Reaching Out!

Where Did You Go? Which of the places on this page did you go to this month? What did you do there? Share with a classmate.

Ⓐ SHOPPING AT THE MALL

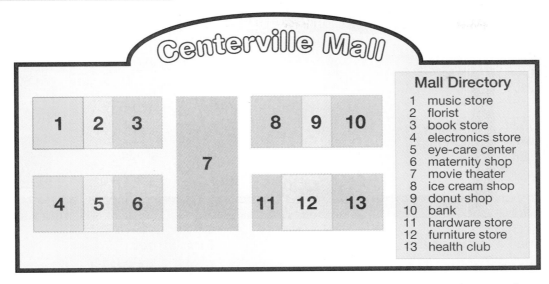

Centerville Mall

| 1 | 2 | 3 |

| 7 |

| 8 | 9 | 10 |

| 4 | 5 | 6 |

| 11 | 12 | 13 |

Mall Directory
1 music store
2 florist
3 book store
4 electronics store
5 eye-care center
6 maternity shop
7 movie theater
8 ice cream shop
9 donut shop
10 bank
11 hardware store
12 furniture store
13 health club

Look at the map of the Centerville Mall. Answer the questions. Write the number of the place.

1. Where can you buy ice cream? __8__
2. Where can you exercise? ____
3. Where can you buy a computer? ____
4. Where can you have coffee? ____
5. Where can you see a movie? ____
6. Where can you buy books? ____
7. Where can you buy tools? ____

8. Where can you buy flowers? ____
9. Where can you get money? ____
10. Where can you buy a CD? ____
11. Where can you buy eyeglasses? ____
12. Where can you buy a sofa? ____
13. Where can you buy a dress for a woman who is going to have a baby? ____

Ⓑ YOUR SHOPPING HABITS

Fill out the questionnaire. Compare answers with a classmate.

How often do you go to the . . . ?

often = once a month or more

	often	sometimes	never		often	sometimes	never
hair salon	❏	❏	❏	laundromat	❏	❏	❏
hardware store	❏	❏	❏	library	❏	❏	❏
health club	❏	❏	❏	movie theater	❏	❏	❏
ice cream shop	❏	❏	❏	music store	❏	❏	❏

Reaching Out!

Places You Like

People are visiting your town. Recommend a good hotel or motel, a good movie theater, and a good ice cream shop. Compare with a classmate.

PLACES AROUND TOWN IV

A WHAT'S THE PLACE?

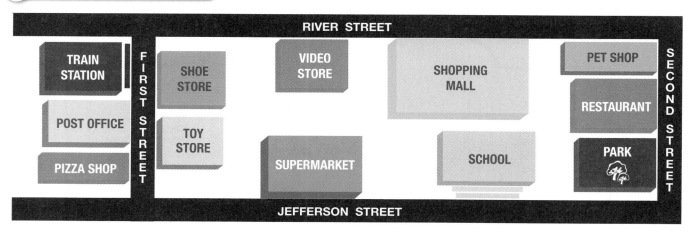

1. You can mail a letter at the _____post office_____ on First Street.
2. You can buy a cat or a dog at the _____ on Second Street.
3. You can get a movie at the _____ on River Street.
4. You can eat lunch at the _____ on First Street or at the _____ on Second Street.
5. You can buy a toy train at the _____ on First Street.
6. You can buy milk, butter, and sugar at the _____ on Jefferson Street.
7. You can buy shoes at the _____ on _____ Street.
8. You can find many stores in the _____ on _____ Street.

B YOUR SHOPPING HABITS

Fill out the questionnaire. Compare answers with a classmate.

How often do you go to the . . . ?

often = once a month or more

	often	sometimes	never		often	sometimes	never
park	❑	❑	❑	shoe store	❑	❑	❑
pizza shop	❑	❑	❑	shopping mall	❑	❑	❑
post office	❑	❑	❑	supermarket	❑	❑	❑
restaurant	❑	❑	❑	video store	❑	❑	❑

Reaching Out!

A Shopping Mall

What stores on pages 78–79 of the Basic Picture Dictionary are in a shopping mall in your town? What other stores are in the shopping mall? Make a list. Compare lists with a classmate.

A PEOPLE, TRANSPORTATION, AND BUILDINGS

Look at pages 80 and 81 of the Basic Picture Dictionary. What people, transportation, and buildings do you see? Fill in the chart.

People	Transportation	Buildings
taxi driver		

B WHERE IS IT?

Look at the picture on page 80 of the Basic Picture Dictionary. Where is everything?

1. The city hall is between the courthouse and the ((police station)   jail).
2. There's a (taxi stand   parking lot) next to the subway station.
3. There are parking meters on the (street   sidewalk).
4. There's a taxi in front of the (courthouse   city hall).
5. There's a (garbage truck   trash container) in front of city hall.
6. There's a (fire alarm box   fire hydrant) next to the mailbox.

C SPRINGVILLE'S BUDGET

This graph shows how the city of Springville spent money in 2008. Look at the graph and complete the chart.

courthouse   fire hydrants   parking lots   parking meters   sewers   sidewalks   street lights

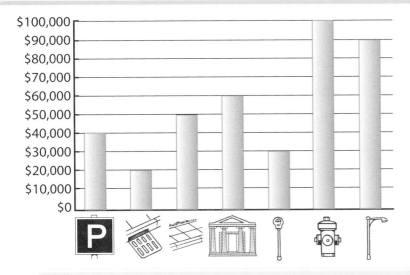

sewers	$20,000
	$30,000
	$40,000
	$50,000
	$60,000
	$90,000
	$100,000

Reaching Out!

A City Street

Find a busy street in your city or town. Look for the items on pages 80–81 of the Basic Picture Dictionary. Make a list of the items you see and compare with a classmate.

A PEOPLE, TRANSPORTATION, AND BUILDINGS

Write each item in the correct group.

| bus driver | fire station | motorcycle | parking garage | street vendor |
| bus stop | ice cream truck | newsstand | pedestrian | |

People	**Transportation**	**Buildings**
bus driver		

B TRUE OR FALSE?

Look at the picture on page 82 of the Basic Picture Dictionary. Decide if the sentences are True (T) or False (F).

__T__ 1. A woman is standing at the bus stop.

____ 2. There's a public telephone in front of the fire station.

____ 3. There's an ice cream truck across from the fire station.

____ 4. A police officer is standing in the crosswalk.

____ 5. The parking garage is next to the drive-through window.

____ 6. A pedestrian is walking a dog.

____ 7. The bus is next to the curb.

C AN INTERSECTION IN YOUR TOWN

Go to an intersection in your city or town. Check (✓) everything you see.

☐ bus	☐ garbage truck	☐ office building	☐ street light
☐ bus stop	☐ ice cream truck	☐ parking garage	☐ street sign
☐ cab	☐ mailbox	☐ parking meter	☐ street vendor
☐ crosswalk	☐ manhole	☐ pedestrian	☐ taxi stand
☐ curb	☐ meter maid	☐ police officer	☐ traffic light
☐ fire hydrant	☐ motorcycle	☐ public telephone	☐ trash container
☐ fire station	☐ newsstand	☐ sewer	

Reaching Out!

Draw and Tell! Draw a picture of the intersection you saw. Then tell a classmate about it.

New Downtown Center Opens

JACKSON, June 4—The new Downtown Center opened yesterday. There's a shopping mall, a hotel, a movie theater, and an apartment building in this beautiful new center.

All four buildings are at the intersection of Commerce Avenue and Main Street. Pedestrians can use crosswalks to go from building to building. The intersection has new traffic lights and a police officer. People can also walk under the street to get to the shopping mall, the hotel, the movie theater, and the apartment building. They all have one basement.

The mall has 40 stores. It has two department stores, an electronics store, a furniture store, a book store, a jewelry store, a toy store, a shoe store, a video store, a maternity shop, and many others. It also has eight restaurants, a health club, and a parking garage. The hotel has 150 rooms, the apartment building has 125 apartments, and there are six screens in the movie theater.

The new downtown center is near the Commerce Avenue subway station. There's also a bus stop nearby at the intersection of Main Street and Elm Street.

1. The new Downtown Center has _____.
   a. one building
   b. two buildings
   c. three buildings
   d. four buildings

2. The new Downtown Center DOESN'T have _____.
   a. a movie theater
   b. a shopping mall
   c. a motel
   d. an apartment building

3. There's a parking garage in _____.
   a. the mall
   b. the hotel
   c. the movie theater
   d. the subway station

4. The hotel has _____.
   a. 40 stores
   b. 125 apartments
   c. four buildings
   d. 150 rooms

5. The mall has eight _____.
   a. shoe stores
   b. restaurants
   c. jewelry stores
   d. book stores

6. The Downtown Center is near the _____ subway station.
   a. Commerce Avenue
   b. Main Street
   c. Elm Street
   d. Jackson

7. There's a _____ at the intersection of Main Street and Elm Street.
   a. subway station
   b. bus stop
   c. parking garage
   d. health club

8. This article is probably from _____.
   a. a book
   b. a dictionary
   c. a newspaper
   d. a notebook

A GROUPING WORDS

Put the words in the correct group.

| average height | heavy | old | slim | thin |
| average weight | middle-aged | short | tall | young |

Age	Weight	Height
middle-aged		

B WHAT'S THE ORDER?

Number the words from 1 (small) to 3 (big).   *Number the words from 1 (small) to 3 (big).*

☐ average height   ☐ tall   1 short   ☐ heavy   ☐ slim   ☐ average weight

Number the words from 1 (young) to 6 (old).

☐ teenager   ☐ girl   ☐ senior citizen   1 infant   ☐ woman   ☐ toddler

C MOTHER AND DAUGHTER

Maria and Rosa are mother and daughter. How are they different? How are they the same? Complete the diagram.

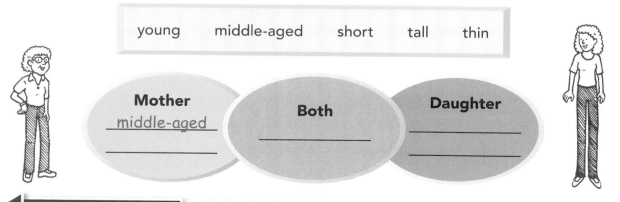

| young | middle-aged | short | tall | thin |

Mother
middle-aged
_____

Both
_____

Daughter
_____
_____

Reaching Out!

Your Family

Bring in photographs of the people in your family or draw a picture. Share with a classmate. Then share with the class. Tell about the people in your photographs or picture.

A OUR CLASS

Anna Valdez   Robert Valente   Elena Vargas

Mario Vega   Carl Vincent   Mei Vu

1. Anna Valdez has (short   (long)) hair.
2. Robert Valente has (curly   straight) hair.
3. Elena Vargas has long (blond   black) hair.
4. Mario Vega has a (mustache   beard).
5. Carl Vincent has (wavy   straight) hair.
6. Mei Vu has (shoulder length   curly) hair.

B FAMILY PHOTOGRAPHS

Read the sentences. Write the name of each person under the correct picture.

Alan is bald.
Nick has straight hair.
Fred has a beard.
Gary has short curly brown hair.

1. ___Fred___   2. _____   3. _____   4. _____

C FATHER AND SON

Manuel and Carlos are father and son. How are they different? How are they the same? Complete the diagram.

| beard   blond hair   heavy   long hair   mustache   short hair   straight hair   thin |

Father
beard
_____
_____

Both
_____
_____

Son
_____
_____
_____

Reaching Out!

Compare yourself to someone in your family. How are you the same? How are you different? Make a diagram like the one above and tell a classmate about it.

You and Your Family

DESCRIBING PEOPLE AND THINGS 1

BASIC DICTIONARY
PAGES 88–89

A OPPOSITES

__c__ 1. new   a. tight
____ 2. fast   b. straight
____ 3. thick   c. old
____ 4. curly   d. thin
____ 5. loose   e. slow

____ 6. tall   f. low
____ 7. neat   g. light
____ 8. wide   h. messy
____ 9. high   i. short
____ 10. heavy   j. narrow

B SAME OR OPPOSITE?

Write S if the words have the same meaning. Write O if the words are opposites.

__O__ 1. good   bad
____ 2. big   large
____ 3. hot   cold
____ 4. thin   skinny

____ 5. small   little
____ 6. straight   crooked
____ 7. dark   light
____ 8. fat   heavy

C WHICH WORD DOESN'T BELONG?

1. car: a. old   b. slow   (c.) skinny
2. pants: a. curly   b. loose   c. long
3. room: a. dark   b. young   c. large
4. hair: a. straight   b. crooked   c. short
5. train: a. fat   b. fast   c. long
6. coffee pot: a. hot   b. new   c. young
7. children: a. good   b. low   c. short

D PEOPLE AND THINGS YOU KNOW

Check (✓) the words that describe . . .

1. your house or apartment: ____ bad ____ neat ____ messy ____ hot ____ cold ____ new ____ old ____ large ____ small ____ good

2. your street: ____ long ____ short ____ wide ____ narrow ____ straight ____ crooked ____ good ____ bad ____ dark ____ light

3. a good friend: ____ tall ____ short ____ heavy ____ thin ____ young ____ old

Reaching Out!

Write About It   Write about one of these people or things you know. Read your description to a classmate.

54

DESCRIBING PEOPLE AND THINGS II

A OPPOSITES

_d_ 1. easy   a. dirty
____ 2. clean   b. wet
____ 3. fancy   c. plain
____ 4. dry   d. difficult

____ 5. shiny   e. full
____ 6. rich   f. handsome
____ 7. empty   g. poor
____ 8. ugly   h. dull

B SAME OR OPPOSITE?

Write S if the words have the same meaning. Write O if the words are opposites.

_O_ 1. open   closed
____ 2. cheap   inexpensive
____ 3. married single

____ 4. rich   wealthy
____ 5. smooth rough
____ 6. noisy   loud

C PEOPLE AND THINGS YOU KNOW

Check (✓) the words that describe . . .

1. you: ____ noisy ____ quiet ____ rich ____ poor ____ pretty
               ____ handsome ____ honest ____ married ____ single

2. your clothes: ____ fancy ____ plain ____ expensive ____ inexpensive
               ____ comfortable ____ uncomfortable

Write about someone or something you know. Read your description to a classmate.

Reaching Out!

Write About It

D YOUR ENGLISH CLASS

Fill out this evaluation form about your English class.

Class Evaluation

	YES	NO		YES	NO
1. My class is very large.	[ ]	[ ]	5. My classroom is neat and clean.	[ ]	[ ]
2. My teacher speaks very fast.	[ ]	[ ]	6. My classroom is very hot.	[ ]	[ ]
3. I feel comfortable in class.	[ ]	[ ]	7. My homework is very difficult.	[ ]	[ ]
4. My class is very noisy.	[ ]	[ ]	8. My class is very long.	[ ]	[ ]

A WHICH GROUP?

annoyed	exhausted	sleepy	tired	unhappy	upset

_____annoyed_____

_____

_____

_____

_____

_____

B PROBLEMS

__c__ 1. I'm cold.

____ 2. I'm exhausted.

____ 3. I'm hungry.

____ 4. I'm sick.

____ 5. I'm full.

a. Have some lunch.

b. Don't finish your dinner.

c. Turn on the heat.

d. Go to bed.

e. Call the doctor.

C HOW DO YOU FEEL TODAY?

Check (✓) Yes or No.

Do you feel annoyed? Yes ☐ No ☐   Do you feel happy? Yes ☐ No ☐

Do you feel disappointed? Yes ☐ No ☐   Do you feel tired? Yes ☐ No ☐

Do you feel excited? Yes ☐ No ☐   Do you feel upset? Yes ☐ No ☐

D HOW OFTEN?

How often do you feel . . . ?

	often	sometimes	never		often	sometimes	never
annoyed	☐	☐	☐	sad	☐	☐	☐
disappointed	☐	☐	☐	sick	☐	☐	☐
miserable	☐	☐	☐	upset	☐	☐	☐

Reaching Out!

English Class

How do you feel in English class? When are you happy? When are you upset? When are you disappointed? When are you annoyed? Discuss in small groups, and then discuss as a class.

A HOW DO THEY FEEL?

Jane writes for a newspaper. She helps people with their problems. Read these letters. Complete each letter with the correct name.

| Afraid | Bored | Frustrated | Homesick | Jealous | Lonely |

Dear Jane,

   I live alone. I don't have any friends in my neighborhood. I don't have any friends at work. What can I do?

_____Lonely_____ 1

Dear Jane,

   Every day is the same. I get up, I go to school, I do my homework, and I watch TV. My life isn't interesting. What can I do?

_____ 2

Dear Jane,

   My boyfriend likes another girl in our class. They sit together in class and help each other. What can I do?

_____ 3

Dear Jane,

   I live in a very bad neighborhood. When I come home from work, the streets are dark and empty. What can I do?

_____ 4

Dear Jane,

   I'm from Brazil. I have a good job in the United States, but I'm not happy. I think about my country all the time. What can I do?

_____ 5

Dear Jane,

   The sink in my apartment is clogged and the bathtub is leaking. I call the landlord every day, but he never comes. What can I do?

_____ 6

B YOUR FEELINGS

Answer the questions with words from pages 94 and 95 of the Basic Picture Dictionary. Use more than one word for each answer.

1. How do you feel when you get a bad grade?   ___upset,_____
2. How do you feel when you make mistakes?   _____
3. How do you feel when you use a computer?   _____
4. How do you feel when you think about your country?   _____
5. How do you feel when it's your birthday?   _____
6. How did you feel on your first day in this country?   _____

Reaching Out!

When do you feel homesick? When are you lonely? When are you frustrated? Share with a classmate.

Homesick, Lonely, and Frustrated

57

A Family Party

Everybody in the Johnson family is very happy today. They're at a family party at the home of Grandma and Grandpa Johnson. The grandparents' home is small, but they have a large backyard. It's a very good place for a family party.

Grandma Johnson is a beautiful woman. She has long wavy gray hair. Grandpa Johnson is tall and thin. He has short curly gray hair and a mustache. He's very handsome. Grandma and Grandpa Johnson have four married children and ten young grandchildren—seven boys and three girls. They're all at the party today. Grandma and Grandpa Johnson are very proud of their family.

Carl Johnson is cooking dinner on the grill. He's Grandpa Johnson's brother. Carl looks very different from his brother. He's short and heavy, and he's bald. Carl likes to cook, and he's very quick. That's good because everybody is very hungry. Carl's wife, Betty, is filling empty pitchers with cold water. It's a hot day, and everybody is thirsty.

Carl and Betty's three children and six grandchildren are also at the party. All sixteen grandchildren are sitting under a big old tree in the backyard. They're listening to music. All the adults are talking. It's a noisy and happy afternoon in the Johnsons' backyard. Everybody is having a wonderful time.

1. The Johnsons' house is a very good place for a family party because _____.
   a. the house is large
   b. the house is small
   c. the backyard is large
   d. it's a beautiful day

2. The grandmother has _____ hair.
   a. straight
   b. wavy
   c. blond
   d. short

3. The grandfather _____.
   a. is heavy
   b. is short
   c. is thin
   d. has a beard

4. Grandma and Grandpa Johnson have three _____.
   a. children
   b. grandchildren
   c. grandsons
   d. granddaughters

5. Grandma and Grandpa Johnson's children are _____.
   a. single
   b. adults
   c. toddlers
   d. teenagers

6. Carl Johnson _____.
   a. doesn't have hair
   b. doesn't like to cook
   c. is tall and thin
   d. is slow

7. Carl's wife is _____.
   a. sitting under a tree
   b. cooking dinner
   c. listening to music
   d. putting water in pitchers

8. Everybody is thirsty because _____.
   a. the weather is hot
   b. the food is hot
   c. the backyard is large
   d. the food is good

A HOW MUCH IS IT?

Look at the supermarket ad and complete the chart.

BEST-BUY $UPERMARKET

$ .50 $ .35 $4.00 $ .45

$ .80 $ .60 $3.75 $ 1.79

Fruit	Price
grapefruit	$1.79
banana	
pear	
watermelon	

Fruit	Price
pineapple	
orange	
lemon	
apple	

B THEY GO TOGETHER

_d_ 1. strawberries   a. raisins
____ 2. oranges   b. limes
____ 3. lemons   c. tangerines
____ 4. grapes   d. raspberries

____ 5. plums   e. nectarines
____ 6. bananas   f. honeydew melons
____ 7. cantaloupes   g. prunes
____ 8. peaches   h. plantains

C LINDA'S FRUIT SALAD

This is Linda's favorite fruit salad.   Look in her refrigerator to see what ingredients she has.   What does she need to buy? Make a shopping list.

Tropical Fruit Salad

3 bananas	1 pineapple
1 coconut	3 apricots
1/2 watermelon	2 apples
2 mangoes	3 pears

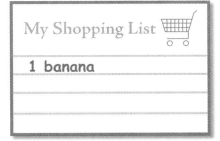

My Shopping List

1 banana

Reaching Out!

What fruits do you like to eat in a fruit salad? What fruits *don't* you like? Ask your classmates what they like and don't like, and compare.

Your Fruit Salad

A HOW LONG CAN YOU KEEP THEM?

Look at the chart and circle the correct answers.

Vegetable	On Shelf	In Refrigerator
mushrooms	----------------	2–3 days
green beans	----------------	3–4 days
parsley	----------------	1 week
garlic	1 month	1–2 weeks
potatoes	1–2 months	1–2 weeks
carrots	----------------	3 weeks

1. You can keep green beans in the refrigerator for 3 or 4 days. (True) False
2. You can keep mushrooms in the refrigerator for 3 to 5 days. True False
3. You can keep parsley in the refrigerator for 7 days. True False
4. You can keep garlic in the refrigerator for one month. True False
5. You can keep carrots in the refrigerator for 21 days. True False
6. You can keep potatoes on a kitchen shelf for 3 months. True False

B FIND THE RECEIPT

Look at the vegetables this person is buying. Put a check (✓) under the correct receipt.

John's Market	
sweet potatoes	1.80
onions	2.79
jalapeños	0.39
cucumber	0.67
corn	1.29
string beans	0.99
Total	$7.93

John's Market	
lima beans	1.39
radishes	1.69
butternut squash	1.19
green peppers	1.38
potatoes	2.00
spinach	2.69
Total	$10.34

John's Market	
acorn squash	1.19
zucchini	1.09
peas	2.39
chili peppers	0.39
yams	1.98
green onions	0.99
Total	$8.03

_____   _____   _____

Reaching Out!

What Do You Buy?

What vegetables do you usually buy when you go shopping?
Bring a shopping receipt to class and circle the vegetables on it.
Compare with a classmate's receipt.

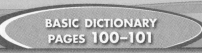
A WHICH DOESN'T BELONG?

1. Poultry: a. turkey   b. shrimp   c. duck
2. Chicken: a. drumsticks   b. thighs   c. tripe
3. Shellfish: a. scallops   b. catfish   c. crabs
4. Meat: a. flounder   b. leg of lamb   c. pork chops
5. Fish: a. trout   b. salmon   c. lobster
6. Seafood: a. halibut   b. ham   c. scallops
7. Beef: a. roast beef   b. steak   c. filet of sole

B LOOK AT THE RECEIPTS

Look at the receipts and answer the questions.

Super Shopper

steak	8.00
chicken wings	4.00
haddock	7.00
scallops	12.00
Total	$31.00

Save More

turkey	14.00
trout	7.00
ham	4.00
lobster	15.00
Total	$40.00

1. How much did this person spend on poultry?
   a. $4.00   c. $8.00
   b. $7.00   d. $12.00

2. How much did this person spend on shellfish?
   a. $4.00   c. $8.00
   b. $7.00   d. $12.00

3. How much did this person spend on meat?
   a. $4.00   c. $8.00
   b. $7.00   d. $12.00

4. How much did this person spend on seafood?
   a. $4.00   c. $12.00
   b. $7.00   d. $19.00

5. How much did this person spend on meat?
   a. $4.00   c. $14.00
   b. $7.00   d. $15.00

6. How much did this person spend on poultry?
   a. $4.00   c. $14.00
   b. $7.00   d. $15.00

7. How much did this person spend on fish?
   a. $4.00   c. $14.00
   b. $7.00   d. $15.00

8. How much did this person spend on seafood?
   a. $4.00   c. $22.00
   b. $15.00   d. $40.00

Reaching Out!

Make a list of all the poultry, seafood, and meat you eat every week.
Compare your list with a classmate's list.

Food for a Week

A WHAT DO YOU EAT?

Look at pages 102 and 103 of the Basic Picture Dictionary. Which foods do you have for breakfast? for lunch? for dinner? Fill out the chart. Compare answers with a classmate.

	Breakfast	Lunch	Dinner
I eat			
I drink			

B DAIRY PRODUCTS AND FAT

When you buy dairy products, choose products that do NOT have a lot of fat. The chart below shows how many grams of fat there are in a cup of each of these foods. Put a check (✓) next to the food that you should choose.

cheese	44 g
cottage cheese	10 g
cream cheese	81 g
butter	181 g

milk	8 g
skim milk	0 g
low-fat milk	2 g
chocolate milk	9 g

sour cream	48 g
yogurt	8 g

1. ____ low-fat milk
   _✓_ skim milk

2. ____ chocolate milk
   ____ milk

3. ____ yogurt
   ____ sour cream

4. ____ cream cheese
   ____ butter

5. ____ cream cheese
   ____ cottage cheese

6. ____ cheese
   ____ cream cheese

C COUNTING CALORIES

Food with a lot of calories can make you heavy. These charts show how many calories there are in a cup of each beverage. Put a check (✓) next to the beverages you should drink.

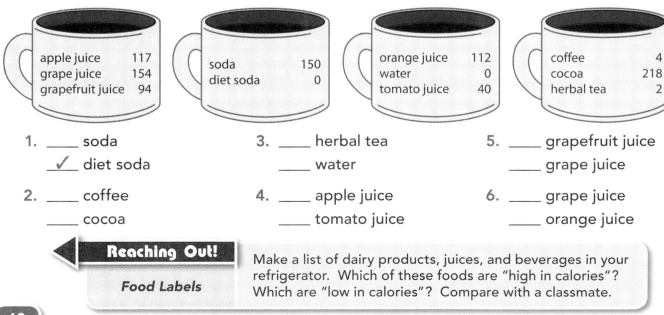

apple juice	117
grape juice	154
grapefruit juice	94

soda	150
diet soda	0

orange juice	112
water	0
tomato juice	40

coffee	4
cocoa	218
herbal tea	2

1. ____ soda
   _✓_ diet soda

2. ____ coffee
   ____ cocoa

3. ____ herbal tea
   ____ water

4. ____ apple juice
   ____ tomato juice

5. ____ grapefruit juice
   ____ grape juice

6. ____ grape juice
   ____ orange juice

Reaching Out!

Food Labels

Make a list of dairy products, juices, and beverages in your refrigerator. Which of these foods are "high in calories"? Which are "low in calories"? Compare with a classmate.

A WHICH GROUP?

American cheese	ham	popcorn	roast beef
bologna	mozzarella	potato chips	Swiss cheese
cheddar cheese	nuts	pretzels	turkey

Meat and Poultry	Cheese	Snack Foods
bologna		

B YOUR CLASSMATE'S FAVORITE FOODS

Interview a classmate. What are your classmate's five favorite deli foods and two favorite snack foods on these charts? Fill in the charts.

Favorite Deli Foods

____ American cheese	____ mozzarella
____ bologna	____ roast beef
____ cheddar cheese	____ salami
____ corned beef	____ Swiss cheese
____ ham	____ turkey

Favorite Snack Foods

____ nuts
____ popcorn
____ potato chips
____ pretzels
____ tortilla chips

C YOUR FAVORITE FOODS

1. What are your five favorite deli foods? _____ _____
   _____ _____ _____

2. What are your two favorite snack foods? _____ _____

D PLANNING A PARTY

Your class is having a party. What are you going to serve? Choose the foods that you and your classmates like.

Our Party Menu

Reaching Out!

Frozen Foods

What frozen foods do you eat? When do you eat them? Compare with a classmate.

A FIX THE SIGNS!

Look at the signs in a supermarket. Cross out the food that doesn't belong in each aisle.

Packaged Goods	Baking Products	Canned Goods	Condiments	Baked Goods
~~mayonnaise~~	flour	soup	cookies	bread
spaghetti	cake mix	mustard	salad dressing	salt
rice	pickles	tuna fish	vinegar	rolls

B WHICH AISLE?

Fill in the missing aisle numbers on the store sign.

1	Canned Goods
2	Packaged Goods
3	Condiments
4	Baked Goods
5	Baking Products

bread	4	flour	☐	rice	☐
cake	☐	ketchup	☐	salt	☐
cake mix	☐	mustard	☐	soup	☐
canned fruit	☐	noodles	☐	spaghetti	☐
cereal	☐	olive oil	☐	spices	☐
crackers	☐	pepper	☐	sugar	☐
English muffins	☐	relish	☐	tuna fish	☐

C SHOPPING WITH COUPONS

Carla is shopping at the store above. She's using these coupons. What's she going to buy? In what aisle is she going to find it? How much is she going to save? Fill out the chart.

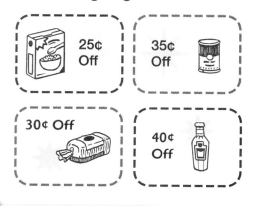

25¢ Off

35¢ Off

30¢ Off

40¢ Off

Food	Aisle	Save
cereal	2	25¢

Reaching Out!

Your Shopping List

You just moved into a new apartment! Your refrigerator and cabinets are empty. Which of the groceries on pages 106 and 107 of the Basic Picture Dictionary are you going to buy? Make a list of ten grocery items. Compare lists with a classmate.

HOUSEHOLD SUPPLIES, BABY PRODUCTS, AND PET FOOD

BASIC DICTIONARY
PAGES 108–109

A WHICH DOESN'T BELONG?

1. Pet Food: a. dog food   (b.) baby food   c. cat food
2. Paper Products: a. soap   b. tissues   c. paper towels
3. Baby Products: a. formula   b. straws   c. wipes
4. Paper Products: a. paper plates   b. napkins   c. aluminum foil
5. Baby Products: a. diapers   b. toilet paper   c. baby cereal

B AMY LEE'S PANTRY

Amy Lee likes to keep the following things in her pantry (a tall storage cabinet in her kitchen).

| baby cereal | diapers | liquid soap | paper cups | sandwich bags | tissues |
| baby food | dog food | napkins | paper towels | soap | trash bags |

This is Amy's pantry. What items does she have? What does she need to buy?

Item	Has	Needs
baby cereal		✓
baby food	✓	
diapers		
dog food		
liquid soap		
napkins		
paper cups		
paper towels		
sandwich bags		
soap		
tissues		
trash bags		

C I USE . . . /I DON'T USE . . .

Which items in this lesson do you use in your home? Which items don't you use?

I use . . .

I don't use . . .

Reaching Out!

Check the household supplies you have in your home. Make two lists. What household supplies do you have? What household supplies do you need?

Your Supplies

A HOW MANY?

Look at the supermarket on page 110 of the Basic Picture Dictionary. How many of the following do you see?

2 shopping baskets	☐ shopping carts	☐ checkout counters
☐ cash registers	☐ scanners	☐ shoppers

B GROUPING WORDS

Put the words below in the correct group.

aisle	can-return machine	checkout line	manager	shopper
bagger	cashier	clerk	scale	

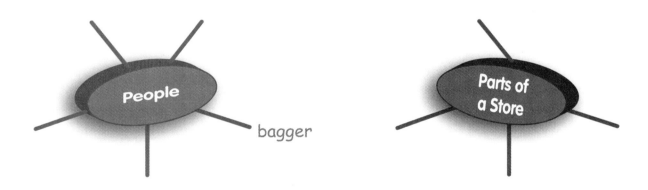

People   bagger

Parts of a Store

C YOUR SUPERMARKET

Go to the supermarket where you shop and answer the questions.

1. How many aisles are there? _____
2. How many checkout lines are there? _____
3. How many express checkout lines are there? _____
4. How many baggers are there? _____
5. How many items can you have in the express checkout line? _____
6. How many can-return and bottle-return machines are there? _____

Reaching Out!

Write About It

Use the information in Exercise C. Write five sentences about your supermarket.

CONTAINERS AND QUANTITIES

BASIC DICTIONARY PAGES 112–113

A WHAT'S THE CONTAINER?

Write each item under the correct container or quantity.

baby food	butter	coffee	lettuce	paper towels	tissues
bananas	cabbage	grapes	mayonnaise	pita bread	toilet paper
beef	cereal	ice cream	milk	rolls	tuna fish

Can	**Box**	**Jar**
coffee		

Roll	**Bunch**	**Half-Gallon**

Package	**Pound**	**Head**

B RECYCLING IN WESTON

Read the Weston Recycling Guide. Put a check (✓) next to things you can recycle. Put an X next to things you can't recycle.

Weston Recycling Guide

 PAPER
- ✓ Newspapers
- ✓ Paper bags
- ✓ Boxes
- Ø No milk or juice cartons

 GLASS
- ✓ Bottles
- ✓ Jars
- Ø No lightbulbs
- Ø No glasses or dishes

 METAL
- ✓ Food cans
- ✓ Soda cans
- Ø No aluminum foil

 ✓   ___   ___   ___   ___

 ___   ___   ___   ___   ___

Reaching Out!

Look in your kitchen for food in the following containers: a can, a jar, a bottle, a box, and a carton. What is in each of the five containers?

Five Containers of Food

A ABBREVIATIONS

Match the measurement with its abbreviation.

_c_ 1. pt.   a. quart
____ 2. tsp.   b. tablespoon
____ 3. Tbsp.   c. pint
____ 4. fl. oz.   d. gallon
____ 5. qt.   e. teaspoon
____ 6. gal.   f. fluid ounce

B FROM SMALL TO BIG

Number from 1 (small) to 6 (big).

	tablespoon		quart
	pint		cup
1	teaspoon		gallon

C MATCHING MEASUREMENTS

1. 2 tablespoons   32 fluid ounces
2. a cup   128 fluid ounces
3. a quart   16 fluid ounces
4. a pint   1 fluid ounce
5. a gallon   8 fluid ounces

D WHAT'S THE WORD?

| cups | teaspoons | quarts | pints |

1. There are 3 __teaspoons__ in a tablespoon.
2. There are 2 _____ in a pint.
3. There are 2 _____ in a quart.
4. There are 4 _____ in a gallon.

E TWO RECIPES

Look at Rita and Ron's recipes for salad dressing. How much of each ingredient do they use? Complete the chart with the correct amounts. (Do not use abbreviations.)

Rita's Salad Dressing
3 Tbsp. vinegar
1 Tbsp. mustard
1 tsp. sugar
6 fl. ozs. olive oil
salt and pepper

Ron's Salad Dressing
4 Tbsp. vinegar
1 tsp. garlic
2 tsp. onions
1 cup olive oil
salt and pepper

Ingredient	Rita uses	Ron uses
vinegar	3 tablespoons	
mustard		--------------------
sugar		--------------------
olive oil		
garlic	--------------------	
onions	--------------------	

Reaching Out!

How Many Fluid Ounces?

Find containers of milk, juice, soup, and cooking oil. Look at the labels. How many fluid ounces does each item have?

UNITS OF MEASURE II

A MATCHING MEASUREMENTS

1. a quarter of a pound   12 ounces
2. half a pound   16 ounces
3. three quarters of a pound   4 ounces
4. a pound   8 ounces

B MATCHING WITH ABBREVIATIONS

__b__ 1. 1/4 lb.   a. 8 ozs.
____ 2. 1 lb.   b. 4 ozs.
____ 3. 3/4 lb.   c. 16 ozs.
____ 4. 1/2 lb.   d. 12 ozs.

C WHAT'S IN THE CONTAINERS?

__d__ 1. a pound of   a. yogurt
____ 2. a quarter of a pound of   b. orange juice
____ 3. a quart of   c. mustard
____ 4. a gallon of   d. cottage cheese
____ 5. a cup of   e. milk
____ 6. half a pound of   f. salad dressing

D COMPARE THE RECIPES

Marco and Jane use the same ingredients in their chili recipes, but they use different amounts. Look at the ingredients and check (✓) who uses more of each.

Marco's Homemade Chili

1 1/2 lbs. ground beef	1 1/4 lbs. tomatoes
7 ozs. kidney beans	8 ozs. carrots
2 Tbsp. jalapeño peppers	1 teaspoon salt
1/4 lb. onions	3 tablespoons olive oil

Jane's Delicious Chili

1 1/4 lbs. ground beef	16 ozs. tomatoes
8 ozs. kidney beans	6 ozs. carrots
2 tsp. jalapeño peppers	2 tsp. salt
6 ozs. onions	4 Tbsp. olive oil

Who Uses More?	Marco	Jane
kidney beans		✓
salt		
carrots		
olive oil		
ground beef		
jalapeño peppers		
tomatoes		
onions		

Reaching Out!

What are the ingredients in your favorite recipe? How much of each ingredient do you use?

Your Favorite Recipe

A PREPARING THE CHILI

This is how Alma prepares her chili. What does she do first? Number the recipe steps 1–6.

Alma's Homemade Chili

1. Chop up the onions, jalapeño peppers, and carrots.
2. Saute the onions, jalapeño peppers, carrots, and ground beef in olive oil.
3. In a large pot, combine the ground beef and beans.
4. Cut up the tomatoes and add to the pot.
5. Add salt and pepper.
6. Let the chili simmer for an hour.

 ___
 ___
 ___

 ___
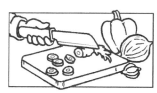 1
 ___

B WHICH DOESN'T BELONG?

1. slice: a. bread   b. mayonnaise   c. cheese
2. peel: a. salt   b. carrots   c. potatoes
3. pour: a. water   b. olive oil   c. roast beef
4. barbecue: a. steak   b. spaghetti   c. fish
5. steam: a. grape juice b. broccoli   c. green beans

C IN YOUR KITCHEN

Write the names of foods you prepare in the following ways. You can write more than one answer.

1. chop up ___onions, tomatoes___
2. grate _____
3. bake _____
4. stir-fry _____

5. broil _____
6. microwave _____
7. roast _____
8. boil _____

Reaching Out!

Preparing Food

Choose a food that you like to eat. List all the ways you can prepare it. Which is your favorite way? Compare with a classmate.

A INGREDIENTS

Match the fast food with the ingredient.

_f_ 1. nachos   a. ground beef
___ 2. french fries   b. lettuce
___ 3. hamburger   c. potatoes
___ 4. ketchup   d. ice cream
___ 5. chili   e. tomatoes
___ 6. salad   f. corn chips
___ 7. milkshake   g. beans

B FOOD, CONDIMENT, OR PAPER?

	food	condiment	paper
relish		✓	
frozen yogurt			
mustard			
straws			
mayonnaise			
hot dog			
lids			

C NUTRITIONAL INFORMATION

This chart shows how many calories and how many grams of fat are in one serving of six popular fast-food items—fried chicken, a salad, salad dressing, a fish sandwich, a cheeseburger, and french fries. Decide if the following sentences are True (T) or False (F).

Calories	Fat
420	24 g.
90	4 g.
170	16 g.
400	18 g.
520	26 g.
525	25 g.

_T_ 1. A fish sandwich has 18 grams of fat.

___ 2. A serving of french fries has 520 calories.

___ 3. A cheeseburger has 26 grams of fat.

___ 4. A serving of fried chicken has 520 calories.

___ 5. A salad has 170 calories.

___ 6. A serving of french fries has 25 grams of fat.

___ 7. A fish sandwich has 525 calories.

___ 8. Salad dressing has 4 grams of fat.

___ 9. A salad with salad dressing has 20 grams of fat.

Reaching Out!

Healthy Choices

What are some fast foods that you like to eat? Make a list. What are some healthy foods that you can eat instead? Make a list.

A **THE SUNLIGHT CAFE**

Look at the signs at this coffee shop. Then write the correct price for each item.

waffles	$3.50
coffee	
toast	
donut	
milk	

egg salad sandwich
hot chocolate
ham and cheese sandwich
tea
muffin

B **BREAKFAST OR LUNCH?**

Which of the following foods do you have for breakfast, lunch, or both? Write them in the correct circle.

bagel	donut	lemonade	muffin	tea
coffee	eggs	milk	pancakes	tuna fish sandwich

Breakfast
_____
_____
_____
_____
_____

Breakfast & Lunch
_____
_____
_____
_____
_____

Lunch
_____
_____
_____
_____
_____

Reaching Out!

Breakfast Foods

What are your five favorite breakfast foods? Do you make them at home, or do you order them at a coffee shop or fast-food restaurant? Make a list. Then compare lists with a classmate.

A WHICH GROUP?

| booster seat | bread basket | chef | dining room | menu | server |
| booth | busperson | diner | host | salad bar | waitress |

People in a Restaurant	
busperson	

Things in a Restaurant	

B WHAT DO THEY DO?

eats the meal
pours the water
prepares the meal
seats the customers
takes the order

1. host or hostess   _seats the customers_
2. customer   _____
3. waiter or waitress   _____
4. busperson   _____
5. chef   _____

C WHAT'S IN THE RESTAURANT?

Think of a restaurant you know. Put a check next to each of these items the restaurant has.

☐ host ☐ booths ☐ high chairs ☐ bread baskets
☐ hostess ☐ tables ☐ booster seats ☐ salad bar

D WHAT ARE THEY DOING?

Look at page 122 of the Basic Picture Dictionary. What is everybody doing?

_d_ 1. The busperson is ____.
____ 2. The hostess is ____.
____ 3. The host is ____.
____ 4. A customer is ____.
____ 5. The chef is ____.
____ 6. The waiter is ____.
____ 7. The waitress is ____.

a. taking an order
b. reading the menu
c. getting a booster seat
d. pouring water
e. working in the kitchen
f. getting a high chair
g. serving the meal

Tell about a restaurant you know. What do you like about the restaurant? What don't you like?

Reaching Out!
A Restaurant You Know

A WHICH GROUP?

bread-and-butter plate	dinner fork	salad fork	soup bowl
butter knife	dinner plate	salad plate	soup spoon
cup	knife	saucer	teaspoon

Dishes
bread-and-butter plate

Silverware

B HOW TO SET THE TABLE

Look at page 124 in the Basic Picture Dictionary and circle the correct answers.

When you set the table, follow these rules:

- The ((forks)   spoons)[1] go on the napkin.
- The knife goes to the right of the (teaspoon   dinner plate)[2].
- The salad fork goes to the left of the (dinner fork   dinner plate)[3].
- The cup goes on the (napkin   saucer)[4].
- The saucer goes to the right of the (wine glass   dinner fork)[5].
- The bread-and-butter plate goes to the right of the (butter knife   salad plate)[6].
- The wine glass goes to the right of the (water glass   soup bowl)[7].

C WHAT'S THE ORDER?

Put the restaurant actions in order. Number the actions from 1 to 8.

☐	The waiter takes the order.	☐	The waiter serves the meal.
1	The busperson sets the table.	☐	The host seats the diner.
☐	The waiter brings the dessert cart.	☐	The customer pays the check.
☐	The busperson pours the water.	☐	The busperson clears the table.

Reaching Out!

Setting the Table

When you set the table for dinner, what dishes and silverware do you use? How do you set the table? Where do you put everything?

A NINA'S FAMILY RESTAURANT

Complete the menu below. Write the heading for each section.

| Appetizers | Desserts | Entrees |
| Salads | Side dishes | |

Nina's Family Restaurant ★

Appetizers

fruit cup	$4.00
tomato juice	$2.00
nachos	$5.25

tossed salad	$3.00
Greek salad	$3.75
Caesar salad	$4.25

meatloaf	$7.25
baked chicken	$7.95
roast beef	$8.95
broiled fish	$8.50

baked potato	$1.95
rice	$1.50
french fries	$1.75
mixed vegetables	$3.95

ice cream	$2.25
apple pie	$2.75
chocolate cake	$2.95
jello	$1.85

B ON THE MENU

Which of these items are on the menu?

antipasto	
apple pie	✓
baked chicken	
baked potato	
broiled fish	
chicken wings	
chocolate cake	
fruit cup	
Greek salad	
ice cream	
jello	
mashed potatoes	
meatloaf	
mixed vegetables	
noodles	
rice	
roast beef	
shrimp cocktail	
tomato juice	
tossed salad	

C THE RESTAURANT BILL

Look at the menu above. Write the names of the foods next to the prices on each of the bills.

Nina's Family Restaurant	
tomato juice	$2.00
	$3.00
	$8.95
	$1.95
	$3.95
	$2.75
Total:	$22.60

Nina's Family Restaurant	
	$5.25
	$3.75
	$7.95
	$8.50
	$1.50
	$1.75
	$2.95
Total:	$31.65

Reaching Out!

You and a classmate are opening your own restaurant. What foods will you serve? What will the prices be? Create a menu and share it with the class.

A Perfect Menu!

Types of Restaurants

When people don't eat at home, they can go to many different kinds of restaurants. There are fast-food restaurants, family restaurants, buffet restaurants, sandwich shops, and many others.

Fast-food restaurants are quick and easy. They serve hamburgers, cheeseburgers, hot dogs, tacos, french fries, chili, and other foods. We call these fast foods because the restaurant usually prepares the food before the customer orders it. Some people eat at the restaurant. The person at the counter gives them their food on a tray. Other people order their food "to go." They receive their food in a bag. Many people like fast-food restaurants because they're quick and cheap.

At family restaurants, customers sit at tables and order food from a menu. A waiter or waitress serves the meal. These restaurants usually serve meat, poultry, and seafood dishes that they cook in different ways. The chef can steam, sauté, bake, boil, broil, fry, stir-fry, or grill different dishes. Typical side dishes are rice, potatoes, and vegetables.

Buffet restaurants are very popular in some places. At these restaurants there is usually a large salad bar with lettuce, tomatoes, and other uncooked vegetables and a hot buffet section with entrees and side dishes. Many buffet restaurants also have a section with fruit such as cantaloupe and watermelon and a section with desserts such as cake and ice cream. Waiters do not bring the food to the table. Customers get up and serve themselves. They pay a set price for everything they eat. They don't pay extra when they go back for more food. Many people love to eat at buffet restaurants, especially when they're hungry!

1. People go to fast-food restaurants because ____.
   a. they're quick
   b. they're expensive
   c. they have salad bars
   d. they have hot buffet sections

2. When a customer orders food "to go," the customer ____.
   a. eats the food at the restaurant
   b. receives the food on a tray
   c. receives the food in a bag
   d. can go back for more food

3. One typical side dish is ____.
   a. a hot dog
   b. rice
   c. poultry
   d. seafood

4. A salad bar at a restaurant DOESN'T have ____.
   a. tomatoes
   b. lettuce
   c. baked potatoes
   d. cucumbers

5. The hot buffet section has ____.
   a. fruit
   b. dessert
   c. salad
   d. entrees and side dishes

6. People pay a set price for everything they eat at ____.
   a. buffet restaurants
   b. family restaurants
   c. fast-food restaurants
   d. sandwich shops

A WHAT COLOR ARE THEY?

Look at the living room on page 46 and the bedroom on page 50 of the Basic Picture Dictionary. Complete the sentences.

Living Room

1. The walls are _____yellow_____.
2. The drapes are _____.
3. The sofa is _____.
4. The armchair is _____.
5. The rug is _____.

Bedroom

6. The walls are _____.
7. The carpet is _____.
8. The curtains are _____.
9. The sheets are _____.
10. The blanket is _____.

B DECORATE YOUR APARTMENT!

You have a new apartment. What colors are you going to use?

Living Room

walls _____
drapes _____
sofa _____
armchair _____
rug _____

Dining Room

walls _____
drapes _____
rug _____
chairs _____
tablecloth _____

Bedroom

walls _____
carpet _____
curtains _____
sheets _____
blanket _____

C COLORS AND CARS

The graph on the left shows the most popular car colors at John's Auto Mart this year. Complete the chart on the right. Write the correct number of cars for each color.

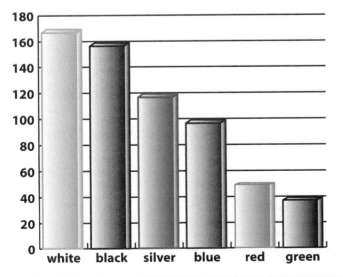

Color	Number of Cars
black	160
blue	
green	
red	
silver	
white	

Reaching Out!

What colors do your classmates like? Take a class survey.
What's the most popular color?

Popular Colors

A WHAT ARE THEY WEARING?

Look at page 130 of the Basic Picture Dictionary. Choose the correct answer.

1. A woman is wearing a blouse and a ((skirt)   shirt).
2. A man is wearing a (vest   jumper).
3. The woman at the bus stop is wearing a blue (jacket   sweater).
4. A woman and a man are talking. The woman is wearing a green (dress   suit).
5. A boy is wearing a white T-shirt and (overalls   shorts).

B A CLOTHING SALE

Look at the ad from The Casual Shop. Write the correct price of each item.

Clothing	Price
dresses	$65
blouses	
shorts	
shirts	
three-piece suits	
T-shirts	
sweaters	
overalls	
pants	
ties	

C DRESS CODE

This is the list of clothing that employees at the Apex Company can and cannot wear to work.

YES!				NO!	
blazers	suits	dresses	sweaters	jeans	leggings
slacks	ties	blouses	turtlenecks	T-shirts	tunics
sport coats	sport shirts	skirts	vests	shorts	overalls

These people work at the Apex Company. Are their clothes okay for work? Write Yes or No.

1. Akiko is wearing a blouse and skirt.   _____Yes_____
2. Tom is wearing jeans and a T-shirt.   _____
3. Rosa is wearing a dress and leggings.   _____
4. Jeff is wearing a suit and tie.   _____
5. Ramon is wearing a turtleneck and slacks.   _____

Reaching Out!

Shopping

You're buying gifts for your friends and family. Look at the ad above.
What are you going to buy? Who are you buying each item for?
How much are you going to spend? Compare with a classmate.

A WHAT ARE THEY WEARING?

Look at page 132 of the Basic Picture Dictionary. Choose the correct answer.

1. The woman with a dog is wearing a (jacket   (coat)).
2. A woman in the park is wearing a (scarf   baseball cap).
3. The vendor is wearing a leather jacket and a (rain hat   cap).
4. The man with the umbrella is wearing a (poncho   trench coat).
5. A boy on a snowboard is wearing a (down vest   parka).

B WHAT ARE PEOPLE WEARING?

What are people in Miami and New York wearing today? Use the words below.

gloves	ponchos	ear muffs	overcoats
trench coats	rain boots	rain hats	mittens

**Miami
60°**

**New York
30°**

It's cool and it's raining in Miami today.
What are people in Miami wearing?

_____trench coats_____

_____

_____

_____

It's cold and it's snowing in New York today.
What are people in New York wearing?

_____

_____

_____

_____

C OUTERWEAR SALE

Forbes Clothing Store is having a big sale. Look at the ad and complete the chart.

FORBES CLOTHING STORE
SALE

Regular Price $12 / Sale Price $8   Regular Price $14 / Sale Price $6

Regular Price $18 / Sale Price $12   Regular Price $8 / Sale Price $5

Regular Price $22 / Sale Price $15   Regular Price $30 / Sale Price $18

Clothing Item	Regular Price	Sale Price
boots	$30	$18
caps		
ear muffs		
gloves		
mittens		
umbrellas		

Reaching Out!

What outerwear do you have? Look in your drawers and closets. Make a list of all your outerwear items. Compare lists with a classmate.

Outerwear Inventory

A WHICH DEPARTMENT?

Which clothing items can you buy in the following departments?

bathrobe	bra	jockstrap	nightshirt	panties	slip
boxer shorts	briefs	nightgown	pajamas	pantyhose	undershirt

Sleepwear ___bathrobe___ _____ _____ _____

Men's Underwear _____ _____ _____ _____

Women's Underwear _____ _____ _____ _____

B WHO WEARS THESE?

bathrobe	bra	jockstrap	nightgown	slip
boxer shorts	camisole	long underwear	pajamas	slippers

Men
___boxer shorts___
_____

Men and Women
___bathrobe___
_____
_____
_____

Women
___bra___
_____
_____
_____

C HOW MUCH WILL THEY SPEND?

Van's Clothing Store is having a big sale.
Look at the ad and answer the questions.

1. Angela is looking for four pairs of pantyhose.
   She'll spend __$20__.
2. Kenji needs three pairs of briefs and three undershirts.
   He'll spend _____.
3. Sophia is looking for three bras and a slip.
   She'll spend _____.
4. Ron needs six pairs of socks and a bathrobe.
   He'll spend _____.

VAN'S CLOTHING STORE

On Sale This Week!

3 for $24

$35

3 for $25

3 for $10

$20
(Buy 2, get one free!)

$14

2 for $10

Reaching Out!

Things to Buy

You need to buy several sleepwear and underwear items. Make a list.
Then look at ads in the newspaper, go to a department store, or look
at a department store website. How much will they cost?

EXERCISE CLOTHING AND FOOTWEAR

BASIC DICTIONARY
PAGES 136–137

A WHAT ARE THEY WEARING?

Look at pages 136 and 137 of the Basic Picture Dictionary. Choose the correct answer.

1. A woman is wearing a sweatshirt and (swimsuit   (sweatpants)).
2. A man is wearing blue (running   lycra) shorts.
3. A woman is wearing a yellow (cover-up   leotard).
4. A man is wearing a red (T-shirt   tank top).
5. A girl is wearing a sweatband and a (jogging   bathing) suit.
6. The (high tops   high heels) are purple.
7. The (thongs   sandals) are pink.
8. The (tennis shoes   running shoes) are white, green, and orange.

B YOUR CLOTHING CHECKLIST

Put a check (✓) next to each item you own.

☐ boots	☐ high-tops	☐ running shorts	☐ sweatshirt
☐ cowboy boots	☐ jogging suit	☐ sandals	☐ swimsuit
☐ flip-flops	☐ leotard	☐ sneakers	☐ tank top
☐ heels	☐ lycra shorts	☐ sweatband	☐ tennis shoes
☐ hiking boots	☐ running shoes	☐ sweatpants	☐ work boots

C WHAT SHOULD THEY WEAR?

It's Saturday morning. These people are going to do different activities today. Look at the clothing checklist above. Help them decide what they should wear. Compare answers with your classmates.

1. Ming is going to go swimming. He should wear _____.
2. Julie is going to play tennis. She should wear _____.
3. Ivan is going to exercise at a health club. He should wear _____.
4. Carla is going to go jogging. She should wear _____.
5. Omar is going to ride his bicycle. He should wear _____.
6. Greta is going to clean her garage. She should wear _____.

Reaching Out!

What kinds of exercise clothing and footwear do you own? Make a list. Then share your list with other classmates. Which items are the most popular?

What's Popular?

A WHICH ITEM?

Choose the correct answer.

1. I'm wearing my favorite (makeup bag   (bracelet)) today.
2. I have two keys on my key (ring   pin).
3. I have twenty-five dollars in my (locket   wallet).
4. I have three dimes in my (chain   change) purse.
5. I carry my textbooks in my (backpack   handkerchief).
6. I keep all my important papers in my (barrette   briefcase).
7. My favorite pieces of jewelry are my engagement ring and my (belt   pearls).

B WHERE DO YOU KEEP THEM?

__b__ 1. I keep my lunch, homework, sweater, and shoes in my ____.   a. change purse
____ 2. I keep dollar bills and credit cards in my ____.   b. backpack
____ 3. I keep pennies, nickels, and dimes in my ____.   c. briefcase
____ 4. I keep lipstick, mascara, and eye shadow in my ____.   d. wallet
____ 5. I keep my books, papers, and pens in my ____.   e. makeup bag

C WHAT'S IN THE STORE?

What can you buy at Marco's Jewelry Store? Write the names of the items to complete the chart.

bracelet   chain   cuff links   earrings   locket   pearls   pin   ring   watch

Marco's Jewelry Store

Jewelry Items	Prices
pin	$250
	$300
	$700
	$150
	$500
	$800
	$350
	$200
	$100

Reaching Out!

Class Inventory

What kinds of jewelry and accessories do your classmates have with them today? Look around the classroom and make a list. Then do a class inventory—make a list of the items and the total number of each item in the classroom.

DESCRIBING CLOTHING

BASIC DICTIONARY
PAGES **140–141**

A) WHICH ONE DOESN'T BELONG?

1. jacket: a. solid green   (b.) pierced   c. extra-large
2. shirt: a. long-sleeved   b. plaid   c. clip-on
3. pants   a. solid blue   b. turtleneck   c. medium
4. socks: a. sleeveless   b. polka-dotted   c. small
5. earrings: a. pierced   b. clip-on   c. plaid

B) COMPLETE THE STORE TAGS

Circle the correct words to complete the store tags for these clothing items.

1.
Style: ((striped)   checked)
Size: (extra–large   sleeveless)
Price: $25.99

2.
Style: (print   solid white)
Size: (medium   extra medium)
Price: $40.99

3.
Style: (short–sleeved   sleeveless)
Size: (polka-dotted   small)
Price: $10.99

4.
Style: (pierced   plaid)
Size: (large   sleeveless)
Price: $42.99

C) FIND THE RIGHT PERSON!

Find somebody in the class who is wearing one of the following clothing items. Write the person's first name in the blank.

_____ pierced earrings   _____ a turtleneck   _____ a solid blue shirt

_____ something plaid   _____ a sleeveless blouse   _____ clip-on earrings

_____ something polka-dotted   _____ a short-sleeved shirt   _____ something striped

Reaching Out!

Describe what someone in your class is wearing today, but *don't* say the person's name. (Describe the color, the patterns, and the materials of the clothing items.) Your classmates must guess who you're talking about.

Guess Who?

A FIND THE OPPOSITE

1. too wide too light
2. too heavy too baggy
3. too fancy too narrow
4. too high too plain
5. too tight too low

B HOW CAN I FIX IT?

1. The shirt is too tight. Lengthen it.
2. The dress is too long. Take it in.
3. The skirt is too short. Let it out.
4. The jacket is too loose. Clean it.
5. The collar is stained. Shorten it.

C SAM'S BARGAIN BASEMENT

At Sam's Bargain Basement the clothes are very cheap because they all have defects. Look at the clothes carefully and find the problems. Then match the items with the defects.

  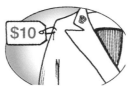 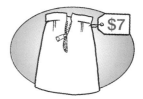

1. The shirt has a broken button.
2. The pants have a stained pocket.
3. The jacket has a ripped zipper.
4. The skirt has a missing collar.

D RETURNING CLOTHES

You can return clothing at Ray's Department Store, but you have to tell the store why you want to return each item. Look at the clothes that people are returning. Complete the chart.

baggy high long ripped stained

RAY'S DEPARTMENT STORE RETURNS		December 15
ITEM	**REASON FOR RETURN**	
Shoes:	The heels are too __high__	.
Shirt:	The collar is _____	.
Jacket:	The sleeve is _____	.
Sweater:	The sleeves are too _____	.
Pants:	They're too _____	.

Reaching Out!

Sewing Survey

Take a class survey. How many students in the class can shorten pants? lengthen sleeves? fix a seam? take in a shirt? let out pants? repair a broken zipper? sew on a missing button? make buttonholes?

THE DEPARTMENT STORE

A WHICH DEPARTMENT?

Where can you find the following items? Write each item next to the correct department.

blender	hamburger	skirt	television
earrings	refrigerator	sofa	tie

Electronics Department	television
Jewelry Counter	
Furniture Department	
Women's Clothing Department	
Household Appliances Department	
Snack Bar	
Men's Clothing Department	
Housewares Department	

B THE STORE DIRECTORY

Look at the store directory. Which floor do you go to when . . .

Departments	Floor
Children's Clothing	3
Customer Pickup Area	1
Customer Service	5
Electronics	4
Gift Wrap Counter	5
Home Furnishings	3
Household Appliances	4
Housewares	4
Jewelry Counter	1
Ladies' Room	5
Men's Clothing	2
Men's Room	5
Perfume Counter	1
Snack Bar	5
Water Fountain	5
Women's Clothing	1

1. you're looking for a blouse? __1__
2. you're looking for a VCR? ____
3. you want something to eat? ____
4. you want to buy a baby a dress? ____
5. you need to use the bathroom? ____
6. you want to buy perfume? ____
7. you want to drink water? ____
8. you want to buy a table? ____
9. you want to put the table in your car? ____
10. you want to buy a tie? ____
11. you want to buy a new refrigerator? ____

Reaching Out!

Departments

Make a list of five things you want to buy in a department store. Which departments will have these items? Go to a department store and see if you are right. Compare lists with a classmate.

85

A WHICH IS FIRST?

Look at the shopping actions below. Circle the one that comes first.

1. a. return   (b.) buy
2. a. try on   b. pay for
3. a. buy   b. get some information about

4. a. buy   b. exchange
5. a. return   b. try on
6. a. exchange   b. pay for

B WHERE CAN YOU FIND THEM?

Look at page 146 of the Basic Picture Dictionary. Complete the sentences.

| label | price tag | receipt | sale sign | size | total price |

1. The discount is on the _____ sale sign _____.
2. The regular price and the sale price are on the _____.
3. The care instructions, the material, and the _____ are on the _____.
4. The price, the sales tax, and the _____ are on the _____.

C WHAT'S ON THE RECEIPT?

Find the information on the following receipts.

women's World Clothes

dress	$60.00
40% off	-$24.00
sale price	$36.00
+ 7% tax	$2.52
cash	$38.52

Waldo's Clothing Mart

jeans	$35.00
30% off	-$10.50
sale price	$24.50
+ 5% tax	$1.23
cash	$25.73

_c_ 1. sale price   a. $60.00
____ 2. regular price   b. –$24.00
____ 3. sales tax   c. $36.00
____ 4. total price   d. $2.52
____ 5. discount   e. $38.52

6. sale price   _____ $24.50 _____
7. regular price   _____
8. sales tax   _____
9. total price   _____
10. discount   _____

Reaching Out!

A Shopping Trip

When was the last time you bought something on sale? What did you buy? Where did you buy it? How much did you spend? What was the discount?

A VIDEO OR AUDIO?

Is the item video equipment or audio equipment?

	Video	Audio			Video	Audio
1. tape deck	____	✓		5. boombox	____	____
2. DVD player	____	____		6. VCR	____	____
3. headphones	____	____		7. speakers	____	____
4. radio	____	____		8. camcorder	____	____

B MATCHING EQUIPMENT

Match the item that goes with each piece of video or audio equipment.

_c_ 1. DVD player   a. film   ____ 5. tape recorder   e. answering machine

____ 2. CD player   b. speakers   ____ 6. VCR   f. memory disk

____ 3. stereo system   c. DVD   ____ 7. telephone   g. TV

____ 4. camera   d. CD   ____ 8. digital camera   h. microphone

C A BIG SALE!

Satellite Electronics is having a big sale this week. Look at the ad and complete the chart.

answering machine   boombox   camcorder   camera   cell phone   flash   radio   television

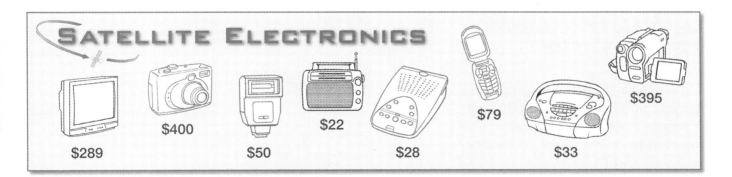

SATELLITE ELECTRONICS

$400 $79 $395

$289 $50 $22 $28 $33

Item	Price
cell phone	$79
	$400
	$28
	$50

Item	Price
	$22
	$33
	$395
	$289

Which items in this lesson do you use? When do you use them?
Compare with a classmate.

Reaching Out!

Using Equipment

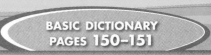
A) WHICH COMPUTER ITEMS?

Choose the correct answer.

1. Put the CD-ROM in the (surge protector (CD-ROM drive)).
2. I'm looking for a flat-panel (screen   disk).
3. I like to type on my new (cable   keyboard).
4. Do you use a mouse or a (joystick   track ball) when you do word processing?
5. What kind of paper do you use in your (printer   disk drive)?
6. Do you want to play a (spreadsheet program   computer game)?
7. My daughter takes her (notebook computer   CPU) to school every day.

B) SHOPPING AT TECH-CITY COMPUTERS

These people shopped at Tech-City Computers. What items did they buy? Check (✓) the items in the chart.

Graciela went to Tech-City Computers last weekend. She bought a CPU, a monitor, and a printer.

Ahmed went to Tech-City Computers yesterday. He bought a notebook computer, a scanner, and a modem.

Lin went to Tech-City Computers today. She bought a mouse and a word-processing program. She wanted to buy a surge protector, but they didn't have any.

Item	Graciela	Ahmed	Lin
	✓		

Reaching Out!

Computers and You

Do you own a computer, or do you sometimes use one? Make a list of all of the parts on the computer you use. If you don't use a computer, draw a picture of a computer and describe it. Compare with a classmate.

The Mall of America

The Mall of America in Bloomington, Minnesota is very large. It has more than 500 stores and 70 restaurants! People from all over the world come to visit this mall.

There are big department stores in each corner of the mall. In each department store, a store directory shows customers where they can find women's clothing, men's clothing, housewares, furniture, household appliances, and all the other departments. These stores have customer service counters where people can return and exchange items. They also have gift wrap counters where someone from the store wraps items that customers are going to give as presents.

There are many small stores on every floor of the mall. Jewelry stores sell rings, necklaces, and earrings. Electronics stores have many different items, from large new TVs to small cell phones and cameras. Shoe stores sell sneakers, boots, sandals, and other kinds of shoes. Music and video stores have CDs, videotapes, and DVDs. There are also book stores, toy stores, computer stores, kitchenware stores, and clothing stores for men, women, and children.

There are big parking lots and parking garages around the mall. Glass elevators take customers from the first floor to the fourth floor. Men's rooms and ladies' rooms are on every floor. There are also many restaurants, snack bars, and food stands where people can get good food to eat. The mall even has a post office. People say it's like a small city. That's why people from all over the world come to Minnesota to see the Mall of America.

1. At the customer service counter, ____.
   a. customers can buy items
   b. customers can return items
   c. customers can eat
   d. someone from the store wraps items

2. ____ sell TVs and cameras.
   a. Toy stores
   b. Video stores
   c. Music stores
   d. Electronics stores

3. Jewelry stores do NOT sell ____.
   a. necklaces
   b. earrings
   c. cell phones
   d. rings

4. Shoe stores do NOT sell ____.
   a. boots
   b. sneakers
   c. sandals
   d. DVDs

5. People at the mall do NOT eat at ____.
   a. kitchenware stores
   b. food stands
   c. restaurants
   d. snack bars

6. The Mall of America has more than five hundred ____.
   a. floors
   b. stores
   c. restaurants
   d. elevators

BASIC DICTIONARY
PAGES 152–153

A MAKE A DEPOSIT

Fill out the deposit slip. Use today's date. Deposit the following amounts:

Cash: $72.50

Check: $100.00

Check: $50.50

DEPOSIT

Manuel Ortega
72 East Street
Los Angeles, CA 90210

Date: _____

BCA Bank of California

⑊0 7 6 3 4 9 2 5 1⑊

| Cash ▶ | | $7 2 5 0 |
| Checks ▶ | | |

Total $

B MAKE A WITHDRAWAL

Fill out the withdrawal slip. Use today's date and the following information:

Account: 300459101

Amount: $50.00

BCA Bank of California   **WITHDRAWAL**

Date

ACCOUNT NUMBER

Name (Print)

Signature _____   Total $

⑊3 1 1 0 9 8 7 9⑊

C WRITE A CHECK

Write a check. Use today's date and the following information:

To: Texas Electric Company

Amount: $42.60

For: May electric bill

Elena Morales
14 Oak Street
Dallas, TX 75205   102

DATE _____

PAY TO THE
ORDER OF _____ $ [   ]

_____ Dollars

BTX Bank of Texas

For _____   _____

⑊746599331⑊888234 22⑊102⑊

D WHAT DO I USE?

<u>b</u> 1. I want to put money in the bank.

_____ 2. I want to get cash from an ATM machine.

_____ 3. I want to pay a bill.

_____ 4. I want to take money out of the bank.

_____ 5. I want to buy something and pay later.

a. check

b. deposit slip

c. withdrawal slip

d. credit card

e. ATM card

Reaching Out!

Your Bank

What bank do you use? How many ATMs, bank officers, and tellers are there at your bank? Compare information with a classmate.

**BASIC DICTIONARY
PAGES 154–155**

A USING AN ATM

Put the actions in order.

- [ ] Select a transaction.
- [ ] Remove your card.
- [ ] Enter your PIN number.
- [ ] Take your transaction slip.
- [1] Insert the ATM card.
- [ ] Withdraw cash.

B HOW DO YOU PAY FOR THINGS?

Put a check (✓) for each way you pay.

	cash	check	credit card	money order
In a supermarket				
In a fast-food restaurant				
In a clothing store				
Household bills				

C HOUSEHOLD BILLS

Alison is paying her bills for the month of December. Write the correct amount under each bill.

December Bills	
Electric Bill	$60.00
Rent	$625.00
Gas Bill	$74.00
Cable TV Bill	$45.30
Telephone Bill	$44.82
Car Payment	$200.00

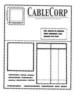

_____   _____   _____

$60.00   _____   _____

D PAY THE BILL

Write a check for $53.42 to Horizon Telephone Company to pay your telephone bill. Use today's date. Don't forget to sign the check!

```
                                              276
                              DATE _____
PAY TO THE
ORDER OF _____   $ [      ]
_____ Dollars
ANB  American National Bank

For _____   _____
⑆746599331⑈888234222⑆276⑈
```

Reaching Out!

Make a list of your household bills. How much do you spend on each bill every month?

Your Bills

A POSTAL RATES

Fill in the missing post office items and prices.

stamp	42¢
sheet of stamps	
	$42
air letter	
book of stamps	
	27¢

B INFORMATION ON AN ENVELOPE

Label the parts of the envelope below.

mailing address   return address   stamp   zip code

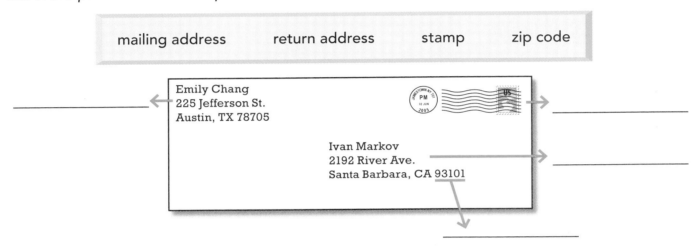

C ADDRESSING AN ENVELOPE

You're sending a letter to this person at the following mailing address. Write the person's mailing address and your return address on the envelope.

Mr. Michael Ortiz
205 Ocean Street
Miami, FL 33147

Reaching Out!

Your Mail

What time does your mail usually arrive? Where does the mail carrier leave it? On a typical day, how many bills do you receive? How many letters? How many packages? How many advertisements? Compare with a classmate.

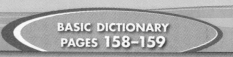
A WHERE CAN YOU FIND THESE?

Check (✓) where you can find each item in a library.

Item	Periodical Section	Media Section	Reference Section
atlases			✓
books on tape			
CDs			
computer software			
dictionaries			

Item	Periodical Section	Media Section	Reference Section
DVDs			
encyclopedias			
magazines			
newspapers			
videotapes			

B BORROWING FROM THE MIDVILLE LIBRARY

Do these people need to pay a fine? Look at the chart and write Yes or No.

Item	Loan Period
book	3 weeks
magazine	3 weeks
videotape DVD	1 week
audiotape book on tape CD software	2 weeks

__Yes__ 1. Bernardo is returning a magazine after four weeks.

_____ 2. Aniko is returning a book after two weeks.

_____ 3. Luis is returning a DVD after 8 days.

_____ 4. Natasha is returning software after 13 days.

_____ 5. Sam is returning a videotape after 9 days.

_____ 6. Amanda is returning an audiotape after 12 days.

C WHERE ARE THEY?

Fill in the correct section and floor for each person.

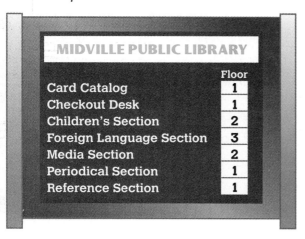

MIDVILLE PUBLIC LIBRARY

	Floor
Card Catalog	1
Checkout Desk	1
Children's Section	2
Foreign Language Section	3
Media Section	2
Periodical Section	1
Reference Section	1

1. Fabio is listening to an audiotape.
   Section ___Media___ Floor _2_
2. Rosa is reading a book in Spanish.
   Section _____ Floor ____
3. Isabel is reading an atlas.
   Section _____ Floor ____
4. José is reading a book to his young son.
   Section _____ Floor ____
5. Carl is reading a newspaper.
   Section _____ Floor ____

Reaching Out!

Go to your local library and find out the following information:
How long can you keep books? magazines? videotapes? DVDs?
audiotapes? books on tape? CDs? software?

Your Library

COMMUNITY INSTITUTIONS

A WHAT NUMBER DO YOU CALL?

Look at the listings in the telephone directory. What number do you call?

CITY OF WATERVILLE	
Ambulance	248-371-9900
City Hall	248-371-7700
Fire Department	248-371-4000
Emergencies	911
Poison Control Center	248-371-4440
Police Department	248-371-2000
Emergencies	911
Recycling Center	248-371-9915

__c__ 1. There's a fire.

____ 2. You want to recycle.

____ 3. Someone drinks poison.

____ 4. You want to talk to the city manager.

____ 5. Your neighbors are making a lot of noise late at night.

____ 6. You're very sick. You need to go to a hospital right now.

a. 248-371-4440

b. 248-371-9900

c. 911

d. 248-371-2000

e. 248-371-9915

f. 248-371-7700

B YOUR EMERGENCY NUMBERS

Look in the telephone book for your city or town. Write the numbers to call.

EMERGENCY NUMBERS	
AMBULANCE	POLICE
FIRE	POISON CONTROL

C WHAT DOES WATERVILLE NEED?

The people of Waterville are having a meeting. They're telling the mayor what their city needs. Complete the sentences.

eldercare workers   emergency room   gym   nursery   police officers   sanitation workers

1. The child-care center needs a new _____ nursery _____ for the infants.

2. We need more _____ to keep our streets clean.

3. We need to build a new _____ for our hospital.

4. We need more _____ to help our senior citizens.

5. We need more _____ to keep our city safe.

6. We need a new _____ in the recreation center.

Reaching Out!

Your Community

Where is a police station, a fire station, and a hospital in your community? What other community institutions are in your city or town? Where are they?

A Post Office Sign

The U.S. Post Office offers the following services and products:

- Use **express mail** to send letters and packages that have to arrive the next day. The letter or package will arrive the next day even when it's a Sunday or a holiday. There is a special envelope at the post office for this service.

- **Priority mail** is a quick and safe way to send letters and packages in the United States. It usually takes between two and three days for the mail to arrive.

- **First class mail** is an inexpensive way to send postcards, letters, checks, and money orders. The items you send can weigh up to 13 ounces. It usually takes between two and three days for the mail to arrive.

- **Parcel post** is an inexpensive way to send packages. It usually takes between two and nine days for the package to arrive.

- Use **certified mail** when you need a receipt to show the date you mailed an item and the date it arrives. You can only use this service with first class or priority mail.

- Buy **money orders**. Don't send cash through the mail.

- Use the **stamp machine** in the lobby to buy single stamps or books of stamps. The lobby is open 24 hours a day.

1. When you send an express letter on Saturday, October first, it will arrive on ____.
   a. Sunday, October second
   b. Monday, October third
   c. Tuesday, October fourth
   d. Wednesday, October fifth

2. Use parcel post to send ____.
   a. letters
   b. money orders
   c. postcards
   d. packages

3. According to the sign, do NOT send ____ in the mail.
   a. checks
   b. money orders
   c. coins and bills
   d. receipts

4. You use a special envelope when you send something by ____.
   a. first class mail
   b. express mail
   c. certified mail
   d. parcel post

5. You can buy ____ in the post office lobby.
   a. books
   b. a stamp machine
   c. stamps
   d. money orders

6. You CAN'T use ____ when you send heavy items.
   a. express mail
   b. first class mail
   c. priority mail
   d. parcel post

BASIC DICTIONARY
PAGES 162–163

A) WHICH WORD DOESN'T BELONG?

1. Face: a. ear   b. nose   c. elbow
2. Leg: a. thigh   b. neck   c. calf
3. Mouth: a. hips   b. tongue   c. gums
4. Face: a. chin   b. chest   c. cheek
5. Hair: a. eyebrows   b. eyelashes c. eyelids
6. Leg: a. knee   b. cheek   c. shin
7. Face: a. jaw   b. lip   c. waist
8. Arm: a. eyebrow   b. elbow   c. shoulder

B) WHAT IS IT?

Write the word.

chest	eyelid	forehead	shoulder	thigh	tooth

1. It's between your neck and arm.   _____shoulder_____
2. It's between your hip and knee.   _____
3. It's in front of the eye.   _____
4. It's inside the jaw.   _____
5. It's between your eyebrows and hair.   _____
6. It's between your neck and abdomen.   _____

C) WHERE DOES IT HURT?

Roberto is at the doctor's office. He's telling the doctor about his problems. Write the number of the sentence next to the part of the body that hurts.

1. My right arm hurts.
2. My chin hurts.
3. My right hip hurts.
4. My chest hurts.
5. My left shoulder hurts.
6. My right knee hurts.

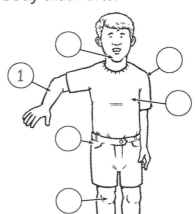

Reaching Out!

What Hurts?

After a busy day of work, what parts of your body hurt? What parts of your body hurt after you exercise? Compare with a classmate.

A) WHAT'S THE MATTER?

Complete the sentences.

foot	hand	lungs	spinal column	stomach	throat

1. My toes hurt. I'm concerned about my _____foot_____.
2. It hurts when I talk. I'm concerned about my _____.
3. My fingers hurt. The doctor is going to check my _____.
4. My back hurts. The doctor is going to check my _____.
5. It hurts after I eat. I'm concerned about my _____.
6. My chest hurts when I exercise. The doctor is going to check my _____.

B) WHAT PART OF THE BODY IS IT?

brain	gallbladder	heart	heel	knuckle	palm	wrist

1. It's between your lungs.   _____heart_____
2. It's between your hand and your arm.   _____
3. It's the part of the foot behind the ankle.   _____
4. It's in the middle of your finger.   _____
5. It's inside your skull.   _____
6. It's under the liver.   _____
7. It's between your wrist and fingers.   _____

C) WHERE ARE THEY?

Arrange the parts of the body from top to bottom.

ankle	pelvis	ribcage	skull

brain	lungs	stomach	throat

_____skull_____   _____

_____   _____

_____   _____

_____   _____

Reaching Out!

Make a list of five body parts that are inside your body. Where are they? Point on your body to show where each one is.

Inside Your Body

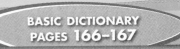
A THE FLU

Read this poster in a doctor's office about the flu. Answer the questions.

Every winter many people get the flu.
How can you tell when you have the flu?
People usually have these symptoms:
- a high fever for three or four days
- a bad cough
- a bad headache
- body aches (for example, a backache)
- a sore throat
- a runny nose
- the chills

Call the doctor when you have:
- shortness of breath
- chest pains
- a high fever for more than 3 or 4 days

1. People usually have a ((sore throat)   toothache) when they have the flu.
2. People usually have a (bloody nose   runny nose) when they have the flu.
3. Call the doctor when you have a fever for (four   five) days.
4. Call the doctor when you have (the chills   chest pains).
5. A (blister   high temperature) is a symptom of the flu.
6. People usually get the flu in the (summer   winter).

B HOW IS YOUR HEALTH?

Are you in good health? Fill out the medical questionnaire below.

Medical Questionnaire

1. Do you often have headaches?   yes ☐   no ☐
2. Do you often have stomachaches?   yes ☐   no ☐
3. Do you often have backaches?   yes ☐   no ☐
4. Do you often have colds?   yes ☐   no ☐
5. Do you often have cramps?   yes ☐   no ☐
6. Do you often have shortness of breath?   yes ☐   no ☐
7. Do you often have chest pains?   yes ☐   no ☐

Reaching Out!

What Do You Do?

What do you do when you have the ailments, symptoms, and injuries on pages 166 and 167 of the Basic Picture Dictionary? When do you call the doctor? When do you go to the emergency room? When do you stay home from school or from work? Compare answers with your classmates.

AILMENTS, SYMPTOMS, AND INJURIES II

BASIC DICTIONARY
PAGES 168–169

A WHAT HAPPENED TO THEM?

Look at pages 168 and 169 of the Basic Picture Dictionary. Complete the sentences.

broke	bruised	burned	twisted	scraped	sprained

1. A man _____sprained_____ his wrist.
2. A man _____ his leg.
3. A woman _____ her knee.
4. A man _____ his arm.
5. A woman _____ her ankle.
6. A man _____ his hand.

B HOW IS YOUR HEALTH?

Are you in good health? Fill out the medical questionnaire below.

Medical Questionnaire

1. Do you sometimes feel faint or dizzy?   yes ☐   no ☐
2. Do you sometimes feel exhausted?   yes ☐   no ☐
3. Do you sometimes have rashes?   yes ☐   no ☐
4. Did you ever break a bone?   yes ☐   no ☐
5. Did you ever have a bad sprain?   yes ☐   no ☐
6. Did you ever have a bad burn or cut?   yes ☐   no ☐

C WHY TELCO'S EMPLOYEES ARE MISSING WORK

*The Telco Company keeps a record of how many employees miss work each month and why.
Read about the following workers. Check (✓) the correct column on the chart.*

	Colds and Fevers	Stomach Ailments	Injuries
1. Mr. Gonzalez broke his leg.			✓
2. Mrs. Hu is congested.			
3. Ms. Phillips feels nauseous.			
4. Mr. Karo burned his hand.			
5. Ms. Hill has cramps.			
6. Mr. Montero is coughing.			
7. Ms. Wang is throwing up.			
8. Mr. Naser bruised his knee.			

Reaching Out!

What do you do when you have the ailments, symptoms, and injuries on
pages 168 and 169 of the Basic Picture Dictionary? When do you call the
doctor? When do you go to the emergency room? When do you stay
home from school or from work? Compare answers with your classmates.

What Do You Do?

A FIRST-AID KIT

Look at the first-aid kit. Find these items. Write the correct letter next to each item.

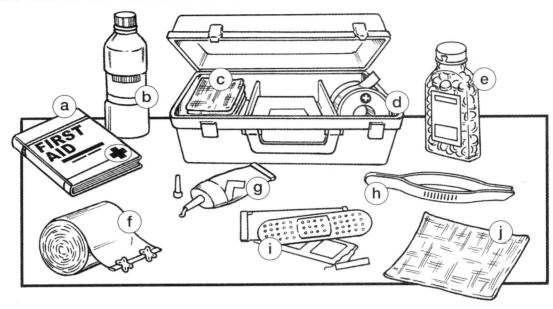

__f__ 1. Ace™ bandage   ____ 4. aspirin   ____ 6. first-aid manual   ____ 9. sterile pad

____ 2. adhesive tape   ____ 5. bandages   ____ 7. gauze   ____ 10. tweezers

____ 3. antibiotic
       ointment
                         ____ 8. hydrogen
                                peroxide

B WHAT CAN THEY USE?

__c__ 1. Ahmed cut his finger.   a. Ace™ bandage

____ 2. Marina burned her hand.   b. tweezers

____ 3. Alonso sprained his wrist.   c. Band-Aid™

____ 4. Naomi scraped her knee.   d. antibiotic ointment

____ 5. Jeff has a splinter (a small piece of wood)   e. hydrogen peroxide
       in his finger.

C WHAT'S THE REMEDY?

__c__ 1. She's bleeding.   a. splint

____ 2. He doesn't have a pulse.   b. rescue breathing

____ 3. He's choking.   c. tourniquet

____ 4. She broke her finger.   d. Heimlich maneuver

____ 5. He isn't breathing.   e. CPR

Reaching Out!

*Your First-Aid
Supplies*

What first-aid supplies do you have? Look in your home and check everything you have. Then make a list of the first-aid supplies you need to buy. Compare lists with a classmate.

A **EMERGENCY OR ILLNESS?**

AIDS	cancer	frostbite	measles
allergic reaction	diabetes	heart attack	overdose on drugs

Medical Emergencies   **Illnesses**

allergic reaction

B **YOUR MEDICAL HISTORY**

Fill out the patient health form.

MEDICAL HISTORY

Name: _____ Date of Birth: _____/_____/_____

Please check (✓) if you had any of the following illnesses.

chicken pox	mumps	heart disease	tuberculosis	cancer
measles	diabetes	asthma	high blood pressure	depression

FAMILY HISTORY:

Please check (✓) if anyone in your family had any of the following illnesses and indicate the relationship (mother, father, grandmother, etc.).

Family history of …	Relationship		Relationship
diabetes		asthma	
heart disease		cancer	
high blood pressure		depression	

RECORD OF IMMUNIZATIONS:

Please check (✓) if you had any of the following vaccinations or tests and fill in the year of the most recent ones.

	Year		Year
measles		tuberculosis test	
mumps		influenza	
chicken pox			

Read the following vaccination guide. Answer the questions.

Vaccination	Who Should Get the Vaccination
Measles and Mumps	All children 12–15 months old Children 4–6 years old
Chicken pox	All children 12–18 months old
Influenza	All children 6–59 months old All adults over 50 years old People with asthma, diabetes, and other serious illnesses Pregnant women Healthcare workers

1. Ramon should get his first mumps vaccination when he's _____ old.
   a. three months   b. thirteen months   c. four years

2. Tomoko is six years old. She should get a vaccination for _____.
   a. measles   b. chicken pox   c. influenza

3. Danielle is a thirty-year-old woman with asthma. She should get a vaccination for _____.
   a. mumps   b. influenza   c. chicken pox

4. Kim should get his second measles vaccination when he's _____ old.
   a. one year   b. two years   c. five years

5. Nina is 6 months old. She should get a vaccination for _____.
   a. influenza   b. chicken pox   c. mumps

D ARE THEY CONTAGIOUS?

A contagious illness is an illness that one person can get from another person.
Check (✓) the correct column.

Illness	Contagious	Not Contagious
asthma		✓
cancer		
diabetes		
high blood pressure		
influenza		
measles		
mumps		
strep throat		

Reaching Out!

Medical Prevention

Look at the list of medical emergencies and illnesses in this lesson. What things can you do to *prevent* some of these emergencies and illnesses so that they don't happen to you?

THE MEDICAL EXAM

BASIC DICTIONARY
PAGES 174–175

A WHAT ARE THEY GOING TO USE?

| eye chart | needle | stethoscope |
| gauge | scale | thermometer |

1. I'm going to take your temperature with this _____thermometer_____.
2. I'm going to listen to your heart with this _____.
3. Look at the _____. I'm going to examine your eyes.
4. Stand on the _____. I'm going to measure your height and weight.
5. I'm going to check your blood pressure with this blood pressure _____.
6. I'm going to draw some blood with this _____.

B TELL ABOUT YOURSELF

1. My height is _____.
2. My weight is _____.
3. My temperature is _____.
4. My blood pressure is _____.

C WHAT ARE THEY DOING?

Read what the doctor and other medical workers are saying. Then match what they're doing.

__d__ 1. "Cover your left eye."
____ 2. "Stand on the scale."
____ 3. "Have a seat."
____ 4. "Don't move."
____ 5. "Breathe in. Breathe out."
____ 6. "Stick out your tongue and say 'Ah.'"

a. taking a chest X-ray
b. asking questions about your health
c. examining your throat
d. examining your eyes
e. measuring your height and weight
f. listening to your heart

D THE DOCTOR OR THE NURSE?

When you have a medical exam in the United States, who usually does the following things?

1. The (doctor   nurse) takes my temperature.
2. The (doctor   nurse) listens to my heart.
3. The (doctor   nurse) checks my blood pressure.
4. The (doctor   nurse) examines my eyes, ears, nose, and throat.
5. The (doctor   nurse) measures my height and weight.
6. The (doctor   nurse) asks me questions about my health.

Reaching Out!

Medical Exams

Tell about a medical exam in your country. What does the doctor do? What does the nurse do? Compare with a classmate.

A MATCHING

_d_ 1. getting a shot
____ 2. cleaning the wound
____ 3. dressing the wound
____ 4. closing the wound
____ 5. sitting in the waiting room

a. alcohol and cotton balls
b. medical history form, insurance card
c. stitches
d. needle
e. gauze and tape

B DOCTOR, DENTIST, OR BOTH?

Who does the following—the doctor, the dentist, or both? Write DO for Doctor, DE for Dentist, or B for Both.

_B_ 1. Who has a receptionist?
____ 2. Who fills your teeth?
____ 3. Who can give prescriptions?
____ 4. Who dresses wounds?
____ 5. Who wears gloves?
____ 6. Who has a waiting room?

____ 7. Who gives Novocaine™?
____ 8. Who drills cavities?
____ 9. Who gives a patient crutches?
____ 10. Who has a hygienist?
____ 11. Who puts your arm in a cast or sling?
____ 12. Who takes insurance?

C WHEN DOES IT HAPPEN?

Put these events in the correct order. Number them from 1 to 6.

☐ The doctor examines her wound.
☐ The doctor gives the patient a prescription.
1 The patient goes into the waiting room.

☐ The doctor closes the wound.
☐ She shows her insurance card to the receptionist.
☐ She fills out a medical history form.

D DID YOU EVER . . . ?

Interview a classmate. Put a check (✓) next to the things that happened to you and to your partner. Tell each other about your experiences.

You	Classmate	You	Classmate	You	Classmate
☐ have stitches? ☐		☐ use crutches? ☐		☐ wear a brace? ☐	
☐ wear a cast? ☐		☐ have a filling without Novocaine? ☐		☐ wear a sling? ☐	

Reaching Out!

Class Survey

Use the information from Exercise D to take a class survey. How many students in the class had stitches? wore a cast? used crutches? had a filling without Novocaine? wore a brace? wore a sling?

A) MATCHING

Match the problem and the advice.

__e__ 1. a cold
____ 2. depression
____ 3. dislocated shoulder
____ 4. sore throat
____ 5. crooked teeth
____ 6. overweight

a. get braces
b. gargle
c. go on a diet and exercise
d. get counseling
e. drink fluids, rest in bed, use a humidifier
f. get physical therapy

B) FIND THE ANSWER!

Look at page 178 of the Basic Picture Dictionary. Choose the correct answer.

1. A woman is ((exercising) gargling).
2. A man is (sleeping   resting) in bed.
3. A young boy is wearing (braces   tests).
4. Dr. Lopez helps patients with (back   ear) problems.
5. A man is drinking (fluids   vitamins).
6. A person uses the (walker   cane) with two hands.
7. The (heating pad   wheelchair) is red.
8. A man is getting (counseling   physical therapy) on his leg.

C) DID YOU EVER . . . ?

Interview a classmate. Put a check (✓) next to the things that happened to you and to your partner.

You	Classmate	You	Classmate
☐ go on a diet?	☐	☐ have physical therapy?	☐
☐ see a specialist?	☐	☐ have surgery?	☐
☐ get acupuncture?	☐	☐ have counseling?	☐
☐ use a heating pad?	☐	☐ wear braces?	☐
☐ use a humidifier?	☐	☐ use a cane or a walker?	☐
☐ use an air purifier?	☐	☐ use a wheelchair?	☐

Reaching Out!

Ask a classmate the questions in Exercise C. When your partner answers *yes*, find out what problem he or she had.

Tell About It

A AILMENTS AND MEDICINE

Match the ailment with the medicine.

__f__ 1. I have a runny nose.

____ 2. I have a cough.

____ 3. I have a headache.

____ 4. I have a stomachache.

____ 5. I have a rash.

____ 6. I have a sore throat.

____ 7. I have dry skin.

____ 8. I have itchy eyes.

a. You should use eye drops.

b. You should use lotion.

c. You should use cough drops.

d. You should take aspirin.

e. You should use throat lozenges.

f. You should use nasal spray.

g. You should use ointment.

h. You should use antacid tablets.

B WHAT'S THE DOSAGE?

tab. = tablet	1x / day = once a day
cap. = capsule	2x / day = twice a day
tsp. = teaspoon	3x / day = three times a day

A   B   C   D   E   F

Look at the medicine labels and choose the correct medicine.

__B__ 1. Take two tablets twice a day.

____ 2. Take one teaspoon three times a day.

____ 3. Take one capsule once a day.

____ 4. Take two teaspoons three times a day.

____ 5. Take one pill twice a day.

____ 6. Take two tablets once a day.

C FOLLOW THE INSTRUCTIONS

Match the instruction with the correct medicine.

__c__ 1. Spray into your nose.   a. aspirin

____ 2. Take two tablets.   b. cough syrup

____ 3. Take two teaspoons.   c. nasal spray

____ 4. Put in each eye.   d. ointment

____ 5. Rub on your skin.   e. eye drops

____ 6. Take one a day.   f. vitamins

Reaching Out!

Medicine and You

What medicines in this lesson do you use when you get sick? Make a list. What other medicines do you use to get better? Compare with a classmate.

A IN A PATIENT'S ROOM

Look at this patient's hospital room. Find the items in the list. Write the correct letter next to each item.

d	1. bed control
	2. bed table
	3. doctor
	4. hospital bed
	5. hospital gown
	6. I.V.
	7. medical chart
	8. patient

B PERSON, PLACE, OR THING?

Is each of these hospital words a person, a place, or a thing? Write PER for Person, PL for Place, and T for Thing.

T bed pan		gurney	midwife
	call button	lab	radiologist
	ER	orderly	surgeon

C WHERE IN THE HOSPITAL?

Look at the floor directory for Brookside Hospital. Write the floor number where you find the following people.

Brookside Hospital

	Floor
Birthing Room	2
Emergency Room	1
Laboratory	4
Nurse's Station	5
Operating Room	3
Radiology Department	6

Person	Floor
surgeon	3
EMT	
nurse	
lab technician	
obstetrician	
X-ray technician	
anesthesiologist	

Reaching Out!

Hospital Workers

Who are the people who work at a hospital? Make a list of all the hospital workers on pages 182 and 183 of the Basic Picture Dictionary. Do you know anyone who has one of these jobs? What does he or she do?

A WHICH PRODUCT?

1. I brush my teeth with ((a toothbrush)   soap).
2. I wash my hair with (sunscreen   shampoo).
3. He uses a (razor   nail file) to shave.
4. I cut my nails with a (comb   nail clipper).
5. I gargle with (dental floss   mouthwash).
6. I use (bubble bath   conditioner) when I take a bath.
7. Nora likes to wear makeup. Every day she puts on rouge and (mascara   deodorant).

B WHICH WORD DOESN'T BELONG?

Cross out the word that doesn't belong.

1. Makeup: blush   eyeliner   ~~conditioner~~   lipstick
2. Shaving: shaving cream   shower cap   electric shaver   razor
3. Teeth: scissors   toothbrush   toothpaste   dental floss
4. Hair: shampoo   blow dryer   comb   sunscreen
5. Washing: soap   nail polish   shampoo   bubble bath
6. Eyes: eyeliner   eye shadow   blush   mascara

C PERSONAL HYGIENE TIPS

Complete the sentences.

| bath | clipper | comb | floss | mouthwash | shampoo | soap |

PERSONAL HYGIENE TIPS

▷ Wash your hands with _____soap_____ [1] and water before and after every meal.
▷ Take a shower or _____ [2] every day.
▷ Wash your hair with a good _____ [3] twice a week.
▷ Wash your brush and _____ [4] every time you wash your hair.
▷ Use a nail _____ [5] to keep your nails short.
▷ Brush and _____ [6] your teeth twice a day.
▷ Gargle with _____ [7].

Reaching Out!

Your Personal Hygiene

You're going on a job interview. Which personal care products in this lesson are you going to use? Compare with a classmate.

BABY CARE

A WHAT DO YOU USE TO . . . ?

Put these words into the correct groups.

baby lotion	bib	diaper pins	ointment
baby powder	bottle	formula	training pants
baby shampoo	cotton swabs	nipple	wipes

Feed the Baby	**Change the Baby**	**Bathe the Baby**
bib		

B BABYSITTING

Erica is a new babysitter. Tell her what to do.

  <u>d</u> 1. The baby's diaper is dirty.
____ 2. The baby is hungry.
____ 3. The baby is bored.
____ 4. The baby is dirty.
____ 5. The baby is crying.

a. Please hold the baby.
b. Please play with the baby.
c. Please bathe the baby.
d. Please change the baby's diaper.
e. Please feed the baby.

C NEWBORN BABY INVENTORY

Check the baby care items Ramona has. Then make a list of the items she needs to buy.

BABY CARE CHECKLIST

☑ baby lotion
☐ baby powder
☐ baby shampoo
☐ cotton swabs
☐ diapers
☐ diaper pins
☐ ointment
☐ pacifier
☐ wipes

Shopping List

baby shampoo
_____
_____
_____
_____

In your opinion, what are the eight most important baby items in this lesson? Compare lists with a classmate.

Reaching Out!

Useful Baby Items

A Community Health Center

The Crosstown Clinic is a large community health center in downtown Southington. People visit the clinic when they have ailments such as an earache or symptoms such as a high fever or a bad cough. They can also go to the clinic once a year for a physical. During this medical exam, a nurse measures a person's height and weight and checks the person's blood pressure. A doctor examines the person and asks questions about his or her health.

When people have medical emergencies and bad injuries (for example, when they break a bone or they're bleeding a lot), they don't go to the community health center. They go to the emergency room at the hospital across the street from the clinic. But sometimes people go to the emergency room with ailments and symptoms that aren't emergencies. Then, the emergency room receptionist sends them across the street to the clinic.

Everyone in the community can use the clinic. The fee (the amount of money a patient pays) depends on the amount of money a patient makes in a year. Patients who don't make much money pay very little. Patients who make a lot of money pay more. Some very poor patients don't pay anything. This sliding scale fee system helps all people stay healthy.

The Crosstown Clinic has ten examination rooms, a large reception area, a radiology department that does patients' X-rays, and a laboratory. The clinic is open weekdays from 8 A.M. to 9 P.M. and from 9 A.M. to noon on Saturdays. The people of Southington are very proud of their health center. It's an excellent public health clinic.

1. A doctor at the clinic _____.
   a. measures the patient's height
   b. checks the patient's blood pressure
   c. measures the patient's weight
   d. examines the patient

2. In the first paragraph, the word *physical* means _____.
   a. an ailment or symptom
   b. a medical exam
   c. a health clinic
   d. a doctor or a nurse

3. The emergency room is _____.
   a. in the clinic
   b. around the corner from the clinic
   c. across the street from the clinic
   d. next to the clinic

4. Patients should go to the emergency room when they _____.
   a. have an earache
   b. break a bone
   c. have a fever
   d. have a bad cough

5. A sliding scale fee system means that _____.
   a. patients pay what they can
   b. rich patients don't pay fees
   c. there's a scale in each exam room
   d. everybody pays the same amount

6. The clinic is open _____.
   a. on Saturday afternoon
   b. on Sunday morning
   c. on Sunday afternoon
   d. on Monday evening

SCHOOL SUBJECTS

**BASIC DICTIONARY
PAGES 188–189**

A WHICH SUBJECT?

1. We paint and draw in ((art)   industrial arts) class.
2. I'm learning to cook in my (shop   home economics) class.
3. My favorite science class is (chemistry   government).
4. We're studying parts of the body in (health   history) class.
5. We're learning about South America in our (biology   geography) class.
6. We do exercises and play basketball in our (physical education   physics) class.
7. Everybody in our school studies a second language. I'm studying (French   math).

B CLASS SCHEDULES

Look at the schedule of classes for students at Bay High School. Complete the sentences below.

Period	10th grade Class	11th grade Class	12th grade Class
1	math	history	English
2	history	English	math
3	geography	business education	government
4	biology	geography	physics
5	English	chemistry	computer science
6	health	math	business education

1. Maria is in 12th grade, and it's 2nd period. She's in _____ math _____ class.
2. Samir is in 10th grade, and it's 2nd period. He's in _____ class.
3. Alexandra is in 11th grade, and it's 5th period. She's in _____ class.
4. Ivan is in 12th grade, and it's 4th period. He's in _____ class.
5. Kira is in 11th grade, and it's 3rd period. She's in _____ class.
6. Tara is in 10th grade, and it's 5th period. She's in _____ class.
7. It's 4th period, and Rafael is in 11th grade. He's in _____ class.
8. It's 5th period, and Max is in 12th grade. He's in _____ class.
9. Gabriella is in 10th grade, and it's 4th period. She's in _____ class.

Take a survey. Ask ten students, "What's your favorite subject?"
What are the most popular subjects in your class?

Reaching Out!

Favorite Subjects

EXTRACURRICULAR ACTIVITIES

A WHAT KIND OF ACTIVITY?

Write the activities in the correct categories.

band	choir	international	orchestra	yearbook
chess	computer	literary magazine	school newspaper	

Music	Writing	Clubs
band		

B WHICH ACTIVITY?

1. I sing in the school (band (choir)).
2. I write for the (school newspaper   A.V. crew).
3. I play the piano in the school (orchestra   pep squad).
4. There are pictures of all the students in our class in the (choir   yearbook).
5. The (debate   community service) club is going to paint an old building near our school.

C THE JEFFERSON HIGH SCHOOL YEARBOOK

Look at the yearbook listings for Amy and Jenny and complete the diagram. What activities did Amy do? What activities did Jenny do? What did they both do?

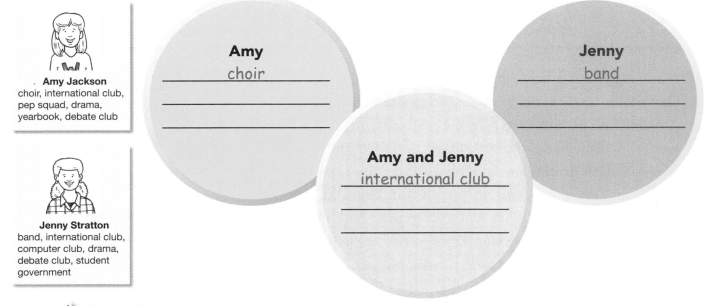

Amy Jackson
choir, international club, pep squad, drama, yearbook, debate club

Jenny Stratton
band, international club, computer club, drama, debate club, student government

Amy
choir
_____

Jenny
band
_____

Amy and Jenny
international club
_____

Reaching Out!

Extracurricular Favorites

Which extracurricular activities in this lesson do you like the most? Why are they your favorite activities? Compare with a classmate.

A ARITHMETIC CHART

What kind of arithmetic problem is it? Put a check (✓) in the correct column.

	Addition	Subtraction	Multiplication	Division
1. $3 \times 6 = 18$			✓	
2. 4 plus 4 equals 8.				
3. 10 divided by 2 equals 5.				
4. $5 - 3 = 2$				
5. $7 + 3 = 10$				
6. 2 times 10 equals 20.				
7. 6 minus 3 equals 3.				
8. $12 \div 3 = 4$				

B ARITHMETIC SIGNS AND WORDS

Write the signs and words to complete the arithmetic problems.

+	−	x	÷	divided by	minus	plus	times

1. 9 __−__ 3 = 6

   Nine _____ three equals six.

2. 4 ____ 2 = 8

   Four _____ two equals eight.

3. 6 ____ 2 = 8

   Six _____ two equals eight.

4. 8 ____ 2 = 4

   Eight _____ two equals four.

C ON SALE!

Write the correct fraction under the sale sign.

1/4	1/3	1/2	2/3	3/4

Sale
75 percent off!

33% off everything in the store!

SALE 66 percent off!

SALE 25% off!

 50% off all men's clothes

1. __3/4__   2. _____   3. _____   4. _____   5. _____

Reaching Out!

Arithmetic Sentences

Write four arithmetic sentences using addition, subtraction, multiplication, and division. Compare with a classmate. Check each other's work.

A WHICH ONE DOESN'T BELONG?

1. lines:	a. curved	**b.** height	c. straight
2. measurements:	a. width	b. length	c. side
3. circle:	a. base	b. radius	c. diameter
4. geometric shapes:	a. square	b. yard	c. rectangle
5. solid figures:	a. pyramid	b. cube	c. triangle

B WHICH SHAPES?

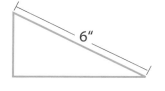
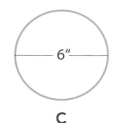

A	B	C

A 1. It's a rectangle.

_____ 2. It's a circle.

_____ 3. It's a triangle.

_____ 4. It has 3 sides.

_____ 5. It has 4 sides.

_____ 6. Its width is 6".

_____ 7. Its diameter is 6".

_____ 8. Its hypotenuse is 6".

_____ 9. It has one right angle.

_____ 10. It has parallel sides.

C ABBREVIATIONS

feet	foot	inch	inches

1. 1" = 1 ___inch___

2. 1' = 1 _____

3. 2" = 2 _____

4. 2' = 2 _____

D AMANDA'S LIVING ROOM

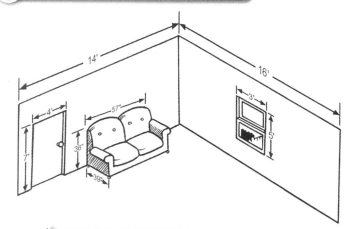

1. The width of the room is ___14 feet___.
2. The length of the room is _____.
3. The height of the door is _____.
4. The width of the door is _____.
5. The width of the window is _____.
6. The height of the window is _____.
7. The length of the sofa is _____.
8. The height of the sofa is _____.
9. The depth of the sofa is _____.

Reaching Out!

Your Living Room

Measure your living room and the furniture in it. Draw a diagram like the one in Exercise D. Show all the measurements. Share your diagram with a classmate and tell about it.

ENGLISH LANGUAGE ARTS AND COMPOSITION

A PARTS OF SPEECH

adjectives	articles	nouns	prepositions	pronouns	verbs

1. read   write   study   _____verbs_____
2. a   an   the   _____
3. in   on   under   _____
4. he   she   they   _____
5. student   teacher   book   _____
6. big   new   happy   _____

B MISSING PUNCTUATION

The teacher corrected the students' sentences. What punctuation did she add?

__h__ 1. What did you do yesterday morning(?)
____ 2. I'm buying apples(,)oranges, and pears.
____ 3. Marla isn't happy(;)she misses her family.
____ 4. I really love my English class(!)
____ 5. I live in Miami(.)
____ 6. He said,(")I'm very tired.(")
____ 7. I need to buy three things(:)milk, juice, and eggs.
____ 8. She(')s nineteen years old.

a. semi-colon
b. colon
c. exclamation point
d. comma
e. apostrophe
f. quotation marks
g. period
h. question mark

C HOW TO WRITE A (COMPOSITION   PREPOSITION)

First ((brainstorm)   edit)[1] some ideas. What are you going to write about? Then organize your (ideas   corrections)[2] and write a first (feedback   draft)[3]. Your composition should have a short (title   adverb)[4] and two or three (apostrophes   paragraphs)[5]. Show your composition to a classmate and get (quotation marks   feedback)[6]. Then make (corrections   semi-colons)[7] and write a (final   first)[8] copy. Pay special attention to punctuation marks. Don't forget to end each sentence with a (comma   period)[9], an (exclamation point   article)[10], or a (question mark   colon)[11].

Reaching Out!

Writing a Paragraph

Write a paragraph about your English class. Brainstorm and organize your ideas. Choose a title. Write a first draft. Get feedback from a classmate. Make corrections. Write a final copy.

LITERATURE AND WRITING

BASIC DICTIONARY
PAGES 198–199

A WHICH ONE DOESN'T BELONG?

1. fiction: novel   short story   (biography)
2. newspaper: article   invitation   editorial
3. computer: postcard   instant message   e-mail
4. non-fiction: essay   autobiography   short story
5. book: poetry   memo   novel
6. post office: postcard   letter   instant message

B MATCHING

Match the sentences with the form of literature or writing that they are from.

__c__ 1. Thank you for the beautiful sweater.   a. autobiography

____ 2. I was born in Ecuador.   b. postcard

____ 3. Our town needs a new hospital.   c. thank-you note

____ 4. We're having a great time in Orlando. See you soon.   d. biography

____ 5. John F. Kennedy was the 35th president of the United States.   e. invitation

____ 6. You're invited to a birthday party.   f. editorial

C YOUR READING HABITS

Fill out the questionnaire. Then compare with a classmate.

How often do you read . . . ? (o = often, s = sometimes, n = never)

	o	s	n
1. poetry	☐	☐	☐
2. short stories	☐	☐	☐
3. newspaper articles	☐	☐	☐

	o	s	n
4. novels	☐	☐	☐
5. biographies	☐	☐	☐
6. magazine articles	☐	☐	☐

D YOUR WRITING HABITS

Fill out the questionnaire. Then compare with a classmate.

How often do you write . . . ? (o = often, s = sometimes, n = never)

	o	s	n
1. letters	☐	☐	☐
2. e-mails	☐	☐	☐
3. postcards	☐	☐	☐

	o	s	n
4. thank-you notes	☐	☐	☐
5. essays	☐	☐	☐
6. reports	☐	☐	☐

Reaching Out!

What We Want to Learn!

Take a class survey. What do students want to learn to write in English? (letters? e-mails? postcards? thank-you notes? essays? reports?) Discuss as a class the results of the survey.

A **LAND OR WATER?**

bay	desert	lake	ocean	plains	river
canyon	island	meadow	peninsula	pond	stream

Land	
canyon	

Water	

B **WHERE ARE THEY?**

Look at page 200 of the Basic Picture Dictionary. Circle the correct answer.

1. The plains are next to the (forest (meadow)).
2. The (plateau   ocean) is above the canyon.
3. There are sand dunes in the (jungle   desert).
4. The waterfall is in the (valley   rainforest).
5. There's (an island   a river) in the ocean.
6. A woman is fishing in a (lake   pond).

C **WHAT'S ON THE MAP?**

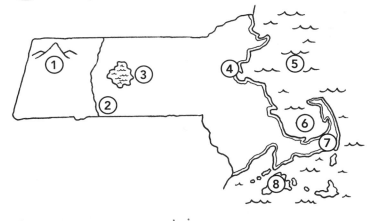

bay	ocean
island	peninsula
lake	river
mountain	seashore

1. _____mountain_____
2. _____
3. _____
4. _____
5. _____
6. _____
7. _____
8. _____

Reaching Out!

Look at a map of the United States. What geographic features can you find? Look for rivers, lakes, peninsulas, bays, islands, and seashores. Where are they? Show a classmate.

Looking at Maps

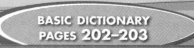

A NEW SCIENCE EQUIPMENT

Ms. Chavez is the science teacher at Lakeville High School. She's ordering new equipment for the science lab. How much is she going to spend for each item? Fill in the prices on her list.

Equipment to Order	
12 test tubes	$7.00
12 flasks	$
12 beakers	$
12 funnels	$
12 graduated cylinders	$
24 Petri dishes	$

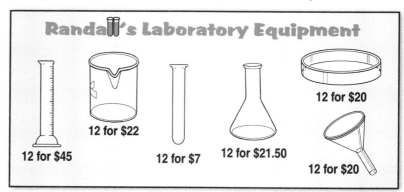

Randall's Laboratory Equipment

12 for $22

12 for $20

12 for $45

12 for $7

12 for $21.50

12 for $20

B WHAT ARE THEY USING?

These students are working in the science lab. What are they using?

1. Lina is looking at slides. She's using a (beaker   (microscope)).
2. Eduardo is doing an experiment with sunlight. He's using (forceps   a prism).
3. Angela is putting chemicals into a test tube. She's using a (slide   dropper).
4. Orlando is picking up a hot test tube. He's using (crucible tongs   a scale).
5. Beatriz is heating some chemicals. She's using a (Bunsen burner   magnet).
6. Ming is pouring liquid into a flask. He's using a (Petri dish   funnel).
7. Reiko is weighing some chemicals. She's using a (balance   computer).

C THE SCIENTIFIC METHOD

Order the procedures in the scientific method.

☐	draw conclusions
1	state the problem
☐	make observations
☐	plan a procedure
☐	form a hypothesis
☐	do a procedure

D SCIENCE EQUIPMENT

Which of the following are made of glass? Put a check (✓) next to each glass item.

☐	balance	☐	test tube
✓	beaker	☐	forceps
☐	magnet	☐	funnel
☐	prism	☐	dropper
☐	scale	☐	Petri dish
☐	flask	☐	Bunsen burner

Reaching Out!

Science Equipment

Which science equipment in this lesson do you/did you use in your science courses? Compare with a classmate.

A Very Special Teacher

Marta Diaz is a very special teacher. She teaches science at Rosemont High School. She teaches four science classes every day: two biology classes for 10th grade students, a chemistry class for 11th grade students, and a physics class for 12th grade students. All of her students say that she is a wonderful teacher.

Ms. Diaz is from El Salvador. Her family moved to the United States when she was 12 years old. When she went to her first day of school in her new country, she didn't speak one word of English. She was a good student and worked hard in all her classes. Science was her favorite subject, but she also liked music. She played in the school band and in the school orchestra, and she sang in the school chorus. When she was in college, she decided to become a science teacher. She had many wonderful teachers who helped her in school. She always remembered those teachers, and she wanted to help students in the same way. She looked for a job in a school with students from many countries. She was happy to find a job at Rosemont High because Rosemont has students from more than thirty different countries.

Ms. Diaz likes to teach, and she also likes to help students outside of class. She works with students on the yearbook, and she meets with students in the international club once a week. Students who don't speak English very well like to go to her classroom after school. Ms. Diaz helps them with their science homework. All the new students from other countries know that she understands how they feel in school because she was once a new student. All the students say that she's their favorite teacher.

1. Marta Diaz does NOT teach _____.
   a. physics
   b. mathematics
   c. biology
   d. chemistry

2. Marta Diaz teaches chemistry to _____.
   a. 9th grade students
   b. 10th grade students
   c. 11th grade students
   d. 12th grade students

3. When Marta Diaz was a student, she DIDN'T _____.
   a. sing in the school chorus
   b. work on the school yearbook
   c. play in the school orchestra
   d. play in the school band

4. Marta Diaz played in the school band because she liked _____.
   a. science
   b. English
   c. biology
   d. music

5. Marta Diaz wanted to teach at a school _____.
   a. with students from many countries
   b. with her favorite teachers
   c. with a good orchestra
   d. in El Salvador

6. New students from other countries like Ms. Diaz because _____.
   a. she understands their languages
   b. she doesn't give any homework
   c. she likes music
   d. she understands their problems

A WHAT DO THEY DO?

| accountant | bricklayer | butcher | computer software engineer | chef |
| baker | businessman | carpenter | construction worker | |

They work with food.	They build things.	They work in an office.
baker		

B JOB OPENINGS

Complete the ads.

| Actor | Baker | Barber | Butcher | Carpenter | Chef |

Actor

Mulberry Theater Company
111 River Drive, Easton
Call Mr. Miller 559-447-4284

Lakeshore Meat Market
10 East Street, Lakeshore
Call Diego 559-447-5670

Henry's Barber Shop
34 Third Ave, Centerville
Call Henry 559-772-3430

Apple Restaurant
77 Main Street, Lakeshore
Call Ms. Vacano 559-447-9296

Reliable Builders
44 Oak Lane, Centerville
Call Sam 559-772-4460

Bella's Bakery
101 Main Street, Easton
Call Bella 559-772-9446

C FROM HIGH TO LOW

The chart on the left shows the average pay for eight different occupations. Number the occupations from 1 (highest salary) to 8 (lowest salary) in the list on the right.

accountant	$61,139
actor	$45,614
artist	$38,294
barber	$21,291
carpenter	$37,181
cashier	$17,077
construction worker	$29,206
cook	$33,129

[1] accountant	[ ] carpenter
[ ] actor	[ ] cashier
[ ] artist	[ ] construction worker
[ ] barber	[ ] cook

Reaching Out!

Interview a Classmate

Interview a classmate about the occupations on pages 204–205 of the Basic Picture Dictionary. In your classmate's opinion, what are the three most interesting occupations? Why?

OCCUPATIONS II

A WHERE DO THEY WORK?

| custodian | dockworker | farmer | food-service worker | hairdresser |
| data entry clerk | factory worker | fisher | garment worker | landscaper |

They work indoors.		They work outdoors.	
custodian			

B THE RIGHT JOB

Which job is right for each person?

1. Julio likes to use a computer.
2. Lana likes to help people.
3. Paul is looking for a good job in a factory.
4. Deepak likes flowers and plants.
5. Natalia likes to clean.
6. Mario likes to drive.
7. Jeff wants to stay home with his children.
8. Eric loves the ocean.
9. Rosa wants to make clothes.

(data entry clerk)	garment worker
health-care aide	dockworker
farmer	foreman
landscaper	janitor
custodian	firefighter
hairdresser	delivery person
homemaker	home attendant
food-service worker	dockworker
garment worker	hairdresser

C JOBS IN THE FUTURE

Read the information. Then look at the pictures. Are these occupations going to have more jobs in the next five years? Write Yes or No.

According to the Department of Labor, there are going to be many new jobs for janitors and food-service workers in the next five years. There are also going to be more jobs for health-care attendants and landscapers. There aren't going to be many new jobs for farmers or garment workers.

 <u>Yes</u>

 _____

 _____

 _____

 _____

 _____

Reaching Out!

You're looking for a job. Look at job listings in the newspaper. Which occupations in this lesson can you find? Which job are you going to apply for? Why? Compare with a classmate.

Finding Jobs

OCCUPATIONS III

A THE RIGHT JOB

Which job is right for each person?

1. Emily is a good boss.
2. Eduardo has good telephone skills.
3. Greta wants to work in a doctor's office.
4. Erica likes to fly planes.
5. Daniel likes to clean.
6. Mohammed likes cars and trucks.

medical assistant   (manager)
receptionist   machine operator
police officer   physician assistant
pilot   manicurist
mover   housekeeper
lawyer   mechanic

B JOB OPENINGS

Complete the ads.

Housekeeper   Machine Operator   Manicurist   Mechanic   Medical Assistant   Pilot

Manicurist
Nina's Nail Salon
404 East Street, Fairfield
Call Nina 352-662-7404

_____
The Belmont Hotel
10 Maple Street, Melrose
Call Mr. Blanco 352-662-4000

_____
Pete's Garage
162 Grove Street, Spring Hill
Call Pete 352-772-3430

_____
Dr. Nadine Gomez
121 Central Street, Melrose
Call Melanie 352-449-3327

_____
Federal Footwear Factory
44 Ninth Avenue, Spring Hill
Call Ms. Hill 352-772-7274

_____
Worldwide Airlines
3400 Gill Avenue, Melrose
Call Mr. Wong 352-662-9401

C FUTURE JOBS

The students in Mr. Diego's class did a class survey to find out the jobs students want. This graph shows the six most popular jobs. How many students want to have each job in the future?

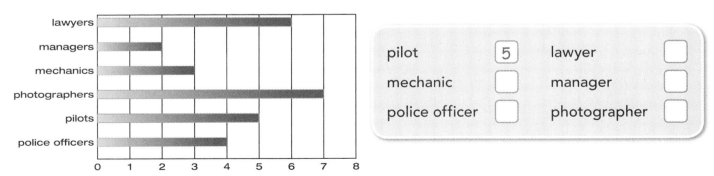

pilot [5]   lawyer [ ]
mechanic [ ]   manager [ ]
police officer [ ]   photographer [ ]

Reaching Out!

Finding Jobs

You're looking for a job. Look at job listings in the newspaper. Which occupations in this lesson can you find? How many job listings for each occupation are there?

OCCUPATIONS IV

A WHAT'S THE OCCUPATION?

1. Ramon is a ((secretary) truck driver) in an office.

2. Barbara works in Ramon's office. She's his (shopkeeper supervisor).

3. Mario is a (teacher sanitation worker) in a school.

4. Ruth is a (veterinarian stock clerk) in a department store.

5. Graciela is a (server servicewoman) in a restaurant.

B GETTING A LICENSE

In Georgia, you have to get a license and pay a fee to work in these occupations.

Occupation	Fees
security guard	$70
teacher	$110
truck driver	$35

Occupation	Fees
veterinarian	$100
welder	$80

Look at the pictures. Write the cost of a license for each occupation. Put an X next to each occupation that doesn't have a license.

 $35   _____   _____    _____

 _____    _____    _____    _____

C JOB OPENINGS AT THE MID-CITY MALL

instructor	salesperson	secretary	server	stock clerk	tailor

Job Openings at the Mid-City Mall
POSITIONS AVAILABLE

BUSINESSES

Tony's Tailor Shop   ___tailor___ 1

Randall's Restaurant   _____ 2

Maxey's Department Store   _____ 3 & _____ 4

The Mall Office   _____ 5

The Apex Language School   Spanish language _____ 6

Reaching Out!

Which of the jobs on pages 210–211 of the Basic Picture Dictionary are good jobs for you? Why?

Good Jobs for You

A WHAT DO THEY DO?

1. Security guards   file.
2. Artists   grow vegetables.
3. Farmers   guard buildings.
4. Secretaries   build things.
5. Carpenters   draw.

6. Janitors   fly airplanes.
7. Pilots   clean.
8. Landscapers   assist patients.
9. Chefs   mow lawns.
10. Nurses   cook.

B YOUR SKILLS

Put a check (✓) next to everything you can do. Then put another check (✓) next to everything you really like to do.

☐ ☐ act
☐ ☐ assemble components
☐ ☐ assist patients
☐ ☐ build things
☐ ☐ clean
☐ ☐ cook
☐ ☐ deliver things
☐ ☐ draw

☐ ☐ drive a truck
☐ ☐ file
☐ ☐ fly an airplane
☐ ☐ grow vegetables
☐ ☐ guard buildings
☐ ☐ manage a restaurant
☐ ☐ mow lawns
☐ ☐ operate equipment

C WHAT ARE THEIR SKILLS?

The students in Mr. Blair's English class have many different skills. Look at the graph below. Complete the sentences about the students.

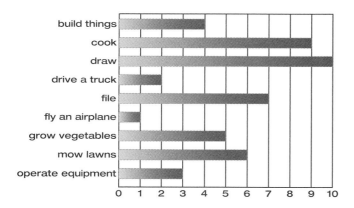

10 students can _____ draw _____.
9 students can _____.
7 students can _____.
6 students can _____.
5 students can _____.
4 students can _____.
3 students can _____.
2 students can _____.
Only 1 student can _____.

Reaching Out!

Skills in Your Class

Take a class skills survey. Ask about eight different skills. Then make a graph like the one above.

A WHAT DO THEY DO?

1. Cashiers —— sew.
2. Dishwashers —— use a cash register.
3. Stock clerks — serve food.
4. Waiters — take inventory.
5. Tailors — wash dishes.

6. Health-care aides — type.
7. Managers — fix things.
8. Secretaries — translate.
9. Interpreters — supervise people.
10. Repairpeople — take care of elderly people.

B WHAT JOB SHOULD THEY APPLY FOR?

Look at the poster for the Oakville Job Fair. Answer the questions.

Oakville Job Fair
Sunday, March 22 at the Oakville Hotel
The following employers will be there:

Oakville Nursing Home looking for . . .
• health-care attendants
• supervisors

River Restaurant looking for . . .
• waiters & waitresses
• cooks

Sam's Appliances looking for . . .
• repairpeople
• cashiers
• stock clerks

Ace Language School looking for . . .
• instructors
• interpreters
• secretary

1. Mohammed can serve food.
2. Elena can teach Spanish.
3. Don can use a cash register.
4. Alonso can take care of elderly people.
5. Brad can fix things.
6. Alicia can prepare food.
7. Rafi can type.

Jobs to Apply For	Employer
waiter	River Restaurant

C YOUR CLASSMATES' SKILLS

Interview three classmates. Ask: "What skills in this lesson do you have?" Then recommend one or more jobs. Complete the chart.

Name	Skills	Jobs

Reaching Out!

Which of the activities on pages 214–215 of the Basic Picture Dictionary do you do at home? Compare with a classmate.

Activities at Home

BASIC DICTIONARY
PAGES 216–217

A WHAT'S THE ABBREVIATION?

available	excellent	Friday	hour	part-time	required
evenings	experience	full-time	Monday	previous	

Dishwashers Wanted

PT[1] and FT[2] positions. $8/hr.[3] No prev.[4] exper.[5] req.[6] Weekends and eves.[7] Call Rita's Restaurant. 590-693-2251.

Receptionist

FT position avail.[8] in busy office. M[9]–F.[10] $10/hr. 2 years exper. req. Excel.[11] benefits. Call Ms. Garcia at 590-689-3311.

1. _____part-time_____
2. _____
3. _____
4. _____

5. _____
6. _____
7. _____
8. _____

9. _____
10. _____
11. _____

B TRUE OR FALSE?

Look at the two ads above. Write T for True and F for False.

Dishwasher Ad

_F_ 1. There are only full-time positions.

____ 2. The pay is $8 an hour.

____ 3. Experience is required.

____ 4. The dishwasher works on Sundays.

Receptionist Ad

____ 5. The job is part-time.

____ 6. The receptionist works on the weekend.

____ 7. Experience is required.

____ 8. The receptionist gets good benefits.

C JOB SEARCH TIPS

ad	application	benefits	dress	experience	note	resume	salary	skills

How to Find a Job

Respond to an _____ad_____ [1].   Talk about your _____ [5]

Prepare a _____ [2].   and _____ [6].

Fill out an _____ [3].   Ask about the _____ [7]

_____ [4] appropriately   and _____ [8].

for your interview.   Write a thank-you _____ [9].

Reaching Out!

Want Ad Abbreviations

Find some want ads in the newspaper and bring them to class. Underline five different abbreviations in your ads. What are the full words for these abbreviations?

A HOW MANY?

Look at the factory on page 218 of the Basic Picture Dictionary. Count how many you see.

2	people on the loading dock	☐	boxes on the forklift
☐	people in the employee lounge	☐	boxes on the dolly
☐	supervisors on the assembly line	☐	time cards

B WHERE IN THE FACTORY?

Look at the factory on page 218 of the Basic Picture Dictionary. Circle the correct answer.

1. The shipping clerk is at the . . .   (loading dock.)   payroll office.
2. The factory workers are sitting at the . . .   shipping department.   work stations.
3. The loading dock is below the . . .   personnel office.   warehouse.
4. The line supervisor is at the . . .   conveyor belt.   freight elevator.
5. The packer is working in the . . .   warehouse.   locker room.
6. The suggestion box is to the right of the . . .   time cards.   union notices.

C PERSON, PLACE, OR THING?

Write these factory words in the correct categories below.

conveyor belt	line supervisor	payroll office	suggestion box
factory worker	loading dock	shipping clerk	time clock
hand truck	packer	shipping department	warehouse

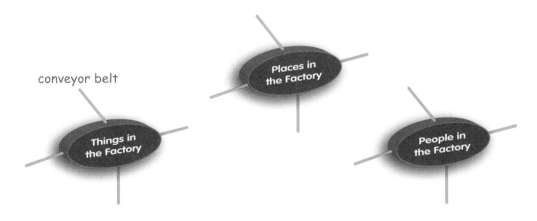

conveyor belt — Things in the Factory

Places in the Factory

People in the Factory

Reaching Out!

Look for factory jobs in the help wanted section of the newspaper.
How many ads can you find for packers, line supervisors, and shipping
clerks? What other factory jobs are there in the newspaper?

Factory Jobs

A AT THE CONSTRUCTION SITE

1. Put those bricks in the ((wheelbarrow)   drywall).
2. I wear a (toolbelt   beam) around my waist.
3. Who is operating the (cement   cement mixer) today?
4. Can I please have that (trowel   pickup truck)?
5. Watch out for that (shingle   crane)!
6. Do we have enough (pipes   trailers)?
7. Could you get me that (scaffolding   tape measure)?

B COMPARING CONSTRUCTION SITES

*Look at the two construction sites below. What tools and machines do you see in Site 1?
What tools and machines do you see in Site 2? What tools and machines do you see in both
sites? Write the items in the correct groups below.*

blueprints	front-end loader	pipes
bricks	jackhammer	tape measure
dump truck	lumber	wheelbarrow

Construction Site 1

Construction Site 2

Site 1
blueprints
_____
_____

Sites 1 & 2
_____
_____
_____

Site 2
jackhammer
_____
_____

Reaching Out!

A Construction Site

Find a construction site in your city or town. What are they
building? What equipment, tools, and materials do you see?
Make a list. Compare with a classmate.

A WHAT DO THEY PROTECT?

1. earplugs	feet	safety glasses
2. goggles	ears	helmet
3. safety boots	eyes	back support
4. hard hat	body	safety earmuffs
5. safety vest	nose and mouth	toe guards
6. respirator	head	mask

B WARNING SIGNS

Match the warning sign with what it means.

A   B   C   D   E   F   G   H

B flammable	___ dangerous	___ poisonous	___ biohazard
___ radioactive	___ corrosive	___ hazardous	___ electrical hazard

C WHICH WORKPLACE IS SAFER?

The following graph compares the safety items at two different companies. Look at the graph. Then put checks (✓) in the chart below to show which company has more of each item.

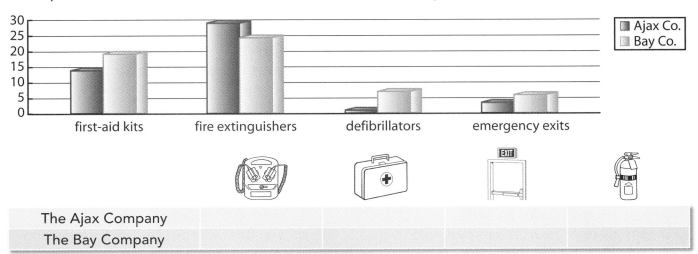

The Ajax Company				
The Bay Company				

Reaching Out!

Work with a small group of classmates. Do a "safety inventory" of your school. What safety items does your school have? How many? What items does your school need? Share your information with people in the school office.

Safety Inventory

Looking for a Job

Emily Chang is 17 years old. She's a student at Carson High School. She wants to be a computer software engineer or a lawyer some day. Her family doesn't have much money, so Emily wants to work after school in the evening and on weekends. She's going to save all of her salary to pay for college.

Every day when Emily walks home from school, she looks at help wanted signs in store windows. Sometimes she sees job notices on the bulletin board at the supermarket for jobs such as gardeners, home health aides, or receptionists, but they're usually full-time jobs. Emily can't apply for these jobs because she goes to school on weekdays. Emily also checks the classified ads in the newspaper. There are many job openings for waitresses, cashiers, and other types of work, but the ads all say "previous experience required."

Last week Emily saw an ad in the newspaper for a salesperson in a computer store. The ad said, "part-time job, no experience required." Emily called the store manager and requested an interview. At the interview, she filled out an application form, and she talked about her computer skills. After the interview she wrote a thank-you note to the store manager.

Emily got the job! She will work from 5 P.M. to 8 P.M. on Tuesday and Thursday evenings and from 10 A.M. to 5 P.M. every Saturday. Emily's first day of work is tomorrow. She's very excited.

1. Emily is looking for a job because ____.
   a. she wants to buy a car
   b. she needs money for college
   c. she needs job experience
   d. she wants to buy a computer

2. Emily is going to start working tomorrow as ____.
   a. a computer software engineer
   b. a lawyer
   c. a store manager
   d. a salesperson

3. Emily did NOT apply for the jobs on the bulletin board because ____.
   a. she doesn't have the skills
   b. she doesn't have the experience
   c. they're full-time jobs
   d. they're part-time jobs

4. Emily found her new job through ____.
   a. a help wanted sign
   b. a classified ad
   c. a job notice
   d. a computer

5. Emily is going to work ____.
   a. every Tuesday morning
   b. every Thursday afternoon
   c. every Saturday
   d. every Sunday

6. This is a good job for Emily because ____.
   a. the job isn't full-time
   b. the salary is very good
   c. the job is near her home
   d. she has experience as a salesperson

A **WHICH GROUP?**

Put these words into the correct groups.

bus	bus stop	conductor	passenger	subway	taxi stand	token
bus driver	cab	fare card	platform	taxi driver	ticket	train

Forms of Transportation	People	Places to Wait	You Pay with These
bus			

B **GOING PLACES**

1. I'm standing on the (track   (platform)) and waiting for the train.
2. You need to show your ticket to the (conductor   passenger).
3. Many people are waiting for the bus at the (bus fare   bus stop).
4. You need to buy a (turnstile   fare card) to get on the subway.
5. The passenger is giving the (transfer   ticket counter) to the bus driver.
6. Where does the Number Fifteen bus go? Look at the (bus route   meter).

C **A CITY BUS**

Read this information about the bus system. Then answer True (T) or False (F).

Using Your Municipal Bus System

Pay when you get on the bus. You can pay with cash or a fare card. When you pay with cash, bus fare is $1.50 (75¢ for senior citizens and children ages 5–11). Bus drivers do not make change. When you pay with a fare card, bus fare is $1.25. Bus drivers do not sell fare cards. You can buy a fare card at any subway station.

There is no extra cost for a transfer. Ask the bus driver for a transfer when you get on the bus and pay your fare.

The first buses leave at 6:00 A.M. on weekdays and at 7:00 A.M. on weekends. The bus system stops service at 1:00 A.M. seven days a week.

__T__ 1. Bus fare for a 65-year-old is 75¢.

____ 2. You have to pay for a transfer.

____ 3. Bus service stops at 1:00 A.M. every day.

____ 4. You can buy a fare card from a bus driver.

____ 5. When you give the driver $2.00, the driver will give you 50¢ change.

Reaching Out!

Transportation

What forms of public transportation do you use? How many times do you use them every week? Make a list. Then compare with a classmate.

A OPPOSITE PREPOSITIONS

Match the preposition with its opposite.

_e_ 1. under   a. off
___ 2. into   b. up
___ 3. on   c. out of
___ 4. down   d. through
___ 5. around   e. over

B GETTING TO ENGLISH CLASS

Check (✓) what you do on your way to English class.

- [ ] I walk across a street.
- [ ] I go through a tunnel.
- [ ] I go past a post office.
- [ ] I go up a hill.
- [ ] I get into a car.
- [ ] I get on a bus.
- [ ] I get on a train.

C TRAVELING

1. Angela walks (through (up)) Central Avenue when she goes to school.
2. Jacob drives (into   over) a bridge every day.
3. Emily walks (around   on) many buildings when she goes to work.
4. Sara drives (off   through) a tunnel every day.
5. Be careful when you get (onto   up) the ferry.
6. I drive (down   out of) a hill every day.
7. Every day Alonso gets (across   off) the bus at Lake Street.

D HOW DONNA GETS TO WORK

This map shows how Donna gets to work. Check (✓) the sentences that are true.

Donna . . .
- [ ] goes under the Bay Bridge.
- [ ] goes around City Hall.
- [ ] goes into City Hall.
- [ ] goes through a tunnel.
- [ ] gets off a bus.
- [ ] walks around the corner.
- [ ] walks past the police station.

Reaching Out!

Getting to School

Draw a map that shows how you get to school. Write directions to school from your home. Compare maps and directions with a classmate.

TRAFFIC SIGNS AND DIRECTIONS

A GETTING A DRIVER'S LICENSE

You want to get a driver's license. Take this practice test. Write the letter under each sign.

A School Crossing
B No U-Turn
C Railroad Crossing
D Merging Traffic
E Slippery When Wet
F No Right Turn
G Pedestrian Crossing
H Handicapped Parking Only

C

___

___

___

___

___

___

___

B INVENTORY OF SIGNS

How many of each sign do you see between your home and your school?

☐ Stop ☐ Detour ☐ One Way ☐ Right Turn Only ☐ Do Not Enter ☐ Yield

C DRIVING DIRECTIONS

Amy lives at 25 Tyler Street. She wants to go to City Hall. She got these directions online. On the map below, draw a line to show the directions from Amy's house to City Hall.

www.MapIt.com

Start: 25 Tyler St., Tampa, FL
End: 127 Bay St., Tampa, FL

🧭 1: Go EAST on TYLER ST. to LAKE ST.

🧭 2: Turn LEFT onto LAKE ST.

🧭 3: Turn LEFT onto DAVIS RD.

🧭 4: Turn RIGHT onto KENT ST.

🧭 5: Turn RIGHT onto SHORE AVE.

🧭 6: Go STRAIGHT until BAY ST.

🧭 7: Go RIGHT onto BAY ST.

🧭 8: Go STRAIGHT. END AT 127 Bay St., Tampa, FL.

Total Time: 10 Minutes   **Total Distance:** 3.1 Miles

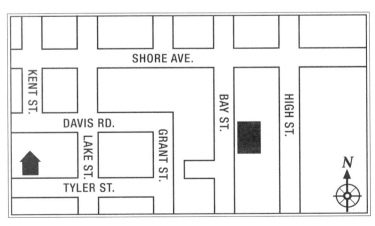

Work with a classmate. Give directions from your school to your home. Your classmate will draw a map to show the directions. Then switch: Your classmate gives directions, and you draw the map.

Reaching Out!

Drawing a Route Map

A AT THE AIRPORT

Match the sentence and the correct group of words.

_d_ 1. These people work at the airport.
____ 2. These are at a security checkpoint.
____ 3. You carry your things in these.
____ 4. You need these to get on the plane.
____ 5. These are places in the airport.
____ 6. These are for your suitcases.
____ 7. You only need these when you go to a foreign country.

a. metal detector, X-ray machine
b. boarding area, baggage claim area
c. baggage claim check, luggage carrier
d. ticket agent, security officer
e. passport, visa
f. ticket, boarding pass
g. garment bag, suitcase

B AIRPORT SIGNS AND MONITORS

Look at the airport sign and monitor. Fill out the chart for the following people.

Ticket Counters	
Airline	Floor
Air America (AA)	3
Blue Sky Airways (BSA)	3
Global Airways (GA)	2
In-Transit Airways (ITA)	2
Safety Airlines (SA)	3
Trans Air (TA)	2

```
            DEPARTURES
FLIGHT    CITY      TIME   GATE
BSA 72    Chicago   2:30   16
GA  48    Dallas    1:25   18
AA  105   Miami     2:15   29
SA  726   New York  2:45   32
TA  402   San Diego 2:00   35
ITA 589   Seattle   2:20   23B
```

Flight	Ticket Counter Floor	Departure Gate	Departure Time
Sandra is on Global Airways flight 48.	2		
Ming is on Blue Sky Airways flight 72.			
Lori is on In-Transit Airways flight 589.			
Rafael is on Air America flight 105.			

C WHICH WORD?

Look at page 230 in the Basic Picture Dictionary and circle the correct word.

1. A man is showing his ((ticket) passport) to the ticket agent.
2. The security officer is checking a (carry-on bag   boarding pass).
3. A woman in the baggage claim area is using a (garment bag   luggage carrier).
4. Passengers at (Gate 40   Gate 41) are going to London.

Reaching Out!

Comparing Airports

Describe two airports you know. How are they the same? How are they different? Compare with a classmate.

The Plane or the Bus?

Isabel and Blanca are sisters. Isabel lives in San Diego, and Blanca lives in Los Angeles. When Isabel visits her sister in Los Angeles, she likes to fly. She drives to the airport and parks her car in the airport garage. It takes 30 minutes to get to the airport. Isabel usually arrives two hours before the flight. She waits in a long line at the check-in counter. The agent takes her suitcase and gives her a boarding pass. Then she waits in another long line and goes through the security checkpoint. She puts her shoes and her carry-on bag on the conveyor belt and walks through the metal detector. After that, she waits at the departure gate for her flight. The flight to Los Angeles usually takes one hour. When the plane arrives in Los Angeles, Isabel goes to the baggage claim area and waits for her suitcase for fifteen minutes or more. Isabel finally meets her sister outside the airport in Los Angeles and they drive to Blanca's house.

When Blanca visits her sister in San Diego, she likes to go by bus. She drives to the bus station and parks her car. It takes 15 minutes to get to the bus station. She usually arrives ten minutes before her bus leaves. There aren't any long lines, and there aren't any security checkpoints. She buys her ticket at the ticket counter and waits for the bus. When the bus arrives, she gives her suitcase to the bus driver and shows her ticket. The bus ride takes 2 1/2 hours. When the bus arrives in San Diego, the driver opens the baggage compartment. Blanca gets her suitcase right away. She meets her sister in the bus station and drives to her house.

Isabel's trip to Los Angeles takes four hours or more. Blanca's trip to San Diego usually takes only three hours. You don't always save time when you take the plane!

1. Isabel usually gets to the airport ____ before the plane leaves.
   a. fifteen minutes
   b. thirty minutes
   c. one hour
   d. two hours

2. Isabel ____ at the check-in counter.
   a. buys a ticket
   b. gets a boarding pass
   c. goes through the metal detector
   d. meets her sister

3. When Isabel gets off the airplane in Los Angeles, she ____.
   a. goes through the security checkpoint
   b. goes through customs
   c. goes to the baggage claim area
   d. goes to the check-in counter

4. Blanca gets to the bus station by ____.
   a. car
   b. taxi
   c. subway
   d. bus

5. The bus driver puts Blanca's suitcase ____.
   a. on a luggage carrier
   b. in the baggage compartment
   c. on a conveyor belt
   d. in the baggage claim area

6. Blanca is on the bus for ____.
   a. thirty minutes
   b. one hour
   c. two and a half hours
   d. three hours

BASIC DICTIONARY
PAGES 232–233

A THE WRONG PLACE!

Cross out the place that doesn't belong.

1. Places to go on a rainy day: concert   play   ~~yard sale~~
2. Places where you can look at art: art gallery   planetarium   museum
3. Places to walk or jog on a sunny day: beach   park   play
4. Places to see animals or fish: flea market   aquarium   zoo
5. Places where you can go shopping: craft fair   movies   swap meet

B A GUIDE TO OAKDALE

Read about the things you can see and do in Oakdale. Answer True (T) or False (F).

> **Haley's Beach:** 3 miles south of Oakdale Center. Good family beach.
>
> **Oakdale Park:** Forest Avenue. Concerts every Thursday.
>
> **Oakdale Botanical Gardens:** 22 East Orange Road. More than 300 kinds of plants. Open 8:00 A.M. to 6:00 P.M. every day. $7.00 adults, $3.00 children.
>
> **Oakdale Science Museum and Planetarium:** 35 Webster Avenue. Open 9:00 A.M. to 6:00 P.M. Mon–Sat, 10:00 A.M. to 5:00 P.M. Sun. $10.00 adults, $5.00 children.
>
> **Oakdale Zoo:** Forest Avenue and State Street. More than 100 different kinds of animals. Open 10:00 A.M. to 6:00 P.M. Tues–Sun. $9.00 adults, $4.00 children.
>
> **John T. Baxter House:** 159 Grand Avenue. Home of the first mayor of Oakdale. Open 11:00 A.M. to 4 P.M. weekends. $5.00 adults, $2.50 children.

  F   1. Haley's Beach is north of Oakdale Center.

_____ 2. You can see movies at Oakdale Park.

_____ 3. The botanical gardens are open from 8:00 A.M. to 6:00 P.M. seven days a week.

_____ 4. The planetarium is on Webster Avenue.

_____ 5. The Oakdale Zoo is open on Monday.

_____ 6. Children pay $5.00 to go to the zoo.

_____ 7. The John T. Baxter House is a historic site.

C WHERE CAN YOU GO?

Put a check (✓) next to the places that are in your community.

- ☐ aquarium
- ☐ art gallery
- ☐ beach
- ☐ botanical gardens
- ☐ historic site
- ☐ mountains
- ☐ museum
- ☐ park
- ☐ planetarium
- ☐ zoo

Reaching Out!
Your Recommendations

Friends are visiting your community this weekend. Which museums, historic sites, parks, beaches, and other places should they visit? Make a list with a classmate.

INDIVIDUAL SPORTS AND RECREATION

BASIC DICTIONARY
PAGES 234–235

A INDOORS OR OUTDOORS?

Where do people usually do these activities? Write each activity in the correct group.

badminton	billiards	boxing	horseback riding	racquetball	tennis
biking	bowling	golf	ping pong	rollerblading	weightlifting

Indoor Activities		Outdoor Activities	
billiards			

B ON THE BALL!

Look at pages 234 and 235 in the Basic Picture Dictionary. Which five sports use one ball?

____bowling____   _____   _____   _____   _____

C WHAT CAN YOU DO?

Read about what you can do at this recreation center. Answer True (T) or False (F).

Fairview Community Recreation Center
Fall Schedule of Activities

Game Room (ping pong, pool, and other games) Mon–Fri 9:00 A.M.–7:00 P.M.; Sat, Sun 12:00 P.M.–5:00 P.M.
Weight Room (weightlifting) Mon–Fri 7:00 A.M.–7:00 P.M.; Sat, Sun 9:00 A.M.–5:00 P.M.
Track (walking, jogging) Mon–Fri 7:00 A.M.–7:00 P.M.; Sat, Sun 9:00 A.M.–5:00 P.M.

Classes

Gymnastics	Mon, Fri 3:00–4:30 P.M.; Tues, Thurs 5:00–6:30 P.M.
Exercise	Mon, Wed, Fri 7:00–8:00 A.M.; Mon, Wed, Fri 6:00–7:00 P.M.
	Tues, Thurs 12:00–1:00 P.M.; Sat, Sun 9:00–10:00 A.M.
Tennis	Mon, Wed 4:00–5:30 P.M.; Sat, Sun 2:00–3:30 P.M.
Martial Arts	Tues, Wed, Thurs 11:00 A.M.–12:00 P.M.
Boxing	Fri, Sat 1:00–2:30 P.M.

__T__ 1. You can play pool in the game room.

____ 2. You can go jogging at the recreation center at 7:00 A.M. on Saturday.

____ 3. There's a gymnastics class at the recreation center on Wednesday.

____ 4. There's an exercise class at the recreation center on Tuesday at 12:00 P.M.

____ 5. Tennis classes are on Monday and Wednesday mornings.

____ 6. There are boxing classes twice a week.

Which activities on pages 234 and 235 of the Basic Picture Dictionary
do you like to do? Make a list. Compare lists with a classmate.

Reaching Out!

Your Activities

TEAM SPORTS

A WHICH GROUP?

Where do people usually do these activities? Write each activity in the correct group.

baseball	basketball	football	hockey	lacrosse	soccer	volleyball

Court	Field	Rink
basketball		

B CLASS SURVEY

The students in Miss Lu's class did a class survey to find out what team sports students like. This graph shows the six most popular sports. Look at the pictures. How many students in the class like these sports? Write the number under each picture.

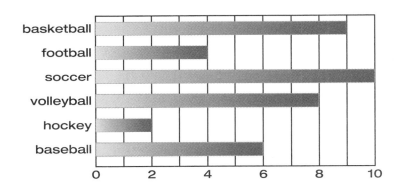

C YOUR FAVORITE SPORTS

Write P for sports you like to play and W for sports you like to watch.

	baseball		football		lacrosse		softball
	basketball		hockey		soccer		volleyball

Reaching Out!

Class Survey

Take a class survey. What are the five most popular team sports in your class? How many students like to watch them? How many students like to play them?

ENTERTAINMENT

A FIND THE TICKETS

Look at the tickets. Write the correct ticket price next to each picture.

$40.00

KELLER AUDITORIUM
PORTLAND OPERA
8:00 P.M. Friday, May 18, 2012
$70.00   R9

COMEDY, ETC.
9:00 P.M. Thursday, June 14, 2012
$30.00

FISHER MUSIC CENTER DETROIT
SYMPHONY ORCHESTRA
7:00 P.M. Saturday, July 21, 2012
$40.00   T12

Best Play of the Year
OCEANS AWAY
2:00 P.M. Sunday, August 25, 2012
$50.00   C15

B WHICH GROUP?

Write each word in the correct group.

adventure	classical	country	hip hop	jazz
cartoon	comedy	drama	horror	rock

Kinds of Music
classical

Kinds of Movies

C YOUR FAVORITES

Fill out the chart with your favorite movie, TV show, and music.

Title of movie:		Kind of movie:	
Name of TV show:		Kind of TV show:	
Title of music/song:		Kind of music:	

Reaching Out!

Favorites

Interview a classmate. What kinds of music, movies, and TV shows
does your classmate like? Take notes. Then share with the class.

Hartsville Entertainment Calendar

Theater
Saying Goodbye
A new play by Rebecca Lee. This drama is about a young woman who leaves her friends and family to start a new life.
Capitol Theater, 452 Main Street.
Sept. 3–Oct. 8, 7:30 P.M. $27.

Dance
James Jefferson Ballet Company
An evening of short ballets.
Majestic Theater, 672 Hanson Place.
Sept 6–7, 8:00 P.M. $30.

Museums and Galleries
Hartsville Art Museum, 224 Parker Street.
"City Streets"—Mark Roma's famous photographs of ten American cities will be at the museum from Sept 3 to Oct 30.
Museum hours: 10:00 A.M. to 6:00 P.M.
$10.00 adults, $8.00 seniors.

Carter Gallery, 189 Windsor Road.
Paintings by Martina Garcia.
Sept. 4–Sept. 30.

Music
Dizzy Martin Jazz Band
Holiday Music Club, 92 Frances Street.
Sept. 5, 7:00 P.M. $20.

Matt and the Motorcycles
Live rock concert at Hartsville Civic Center.
600 Main Street, Sept. 6, 6:30 P.M. $25.

Community Events
Movies in the Park
Hartsville Park, Fifth and Park Street.
Sept. 4, 8:00 P.M.—*Lost in the Mountains*.
An exciting adventure movie.
Sept. 6, 8:00 P.M.—*Happy Times*.
A comedy about high school friends.

Hartsville Crafts Fair, Congress Street.
Sept 5, 9:00 A.M.–4:00 P.M.

High School Baseball Game
Hartsville Pilots play the Greenfield Jets.
Hartsville High School baseball field.
Sept 6, 1:00 P.M. $5.

1. You can hear _____ at the Holiday Music Club.
   a. classical music
   b. popular music
   c. jazz
   d. rock music

2. You can see a play at _____.
   a. the Majestic Theater
   b. the Capitol Theater
   c. the Hartsville Civic Center
   d. Hartsville Park

3. Tickets to the _____ cost $25.
   a. rock concert
   b. play
   c. baseball game
   d. ballet

4. Mark Roma is _____.
   a. a painter
   b. a photographer
   c. an actor
   d. a baseball player

5. *Lost in the Mountains* is _____.
   a. a comedy
   b. a drama
   c. a horror movie
   d. an action movie

6. You can _____ on September 7.
   a. go to a jazz concert
   b. see a movie in the park
   c. see Martina Garcia's paintings
   d. go to a crafts fair

FORMS OF IDENTIFICATION

A WHICH FORM OF IDENTIFICATION?

a   b   c   d   e   f

__e__ 1. All the employees in my company have to wear this while they're at work.

____ 2. Susie is entering kindergarten. Her parents need to show that she's five years old.

____ 3. Victor didn't stop at a stop sign. He needs to show this to a police officer.

____ 4. My school gave this to me when I started to study there.

____ 5. Mark is going to Mexico. He needs to show this to the immigration officer at the airport.

____ 6. Everybody who works and pays taxes in the United States should have this card.

B WHICH FORM?

1. I need to see your (permanent resident card   (driver's license)) to cash your check.
2. Everybody who works here wears (an employee I.D. badge   a work permit).
3. Students show their (birth certificate   student I.D. card) each time they enter the school.
4. An electric bill with your name and address on it is (proof of residence   a visa).
5. Every citizen of the United States can get a U.S. (passport   permanent resident card).

C YOUR FORMS OF I.D.

Look at the forms of I.D. you have. Check (✓) the sentences that are true.

	I have one.	It has my picture.	It has my address.	It has my date of birth.
1. driver's license	☐	☐	☐	☐
2. permanent resident card	☐	☐	☐	☐
3. employee I.D. badge	☐	☐	☐	☐
4. birth certificate	☐	☐	☐	☐
5. work permit	☐	☐	☐	☐
6. social security card	☐	☐	☐	☐
7. student I.D. card	☐	☐	☐	☐

Which forms of identification do you always carry with you? Which forms of identification did you show this week? Where? Compare with a classmate.

Reaching Out!

Your Forms of I.D.

A WHO, WHAT, WHERE?

Look at pages 242–243 of the Basic Picture Dictionary and complete the chart.

Capitol Building   explain the laws   president   Supreme Court justices
chief justice   judicial   representatives   vice-president
enforce the laws   legislative   senators   White House
executive   make the laws   Supreme Court Building

Which branch?	Who?	Which building?	What do they do?
legislative	representatives senators		
			enforce the laws
		Supreme Court Building	

B TRUE OR FALSE?

__T__ 1. Senators work in the Capitol Building.

____ 2. The president is in the executive branch.

____ 3. The cabinet explains the laws.

____ 4. The Supreme Court is in the judicial branch of government.

____ 5. Congressmen and congresswomen enforce the laws.

C YOUR GOVERNMENT OFFICIALS

Who are your government officials right now? Write their names below.

President of the United States   _____

Vice-President of the United States   _____

Chief Justice of the Supreme Court   _____

Senators from your state   _____

Representative from your congressional district   _____

Reaching Out!

Learning About Government

Find the answers to these questions and discuss as a class:
How many United States senators are there? How many United States representatives are there? How many Supreme Court justices are there? How often do people in the United States vote for the president and vice-president? their senators? their representatives?

A WHICH IS CORRECT?

1. The Constitution begins with the ((Preamble)   1st Amendment).
2. The Constitution is the supreme (court   law) of the land.
3. The Bill of Rights is the first (nine   ten) amendments to the Constitution.
4. The 1st Amendment (ended   guarantees) freedom of speech.
5. The 16th Amendment (established   ended) income taxes.
6. The (1st   15th) Amendment guarantees freedom of religion.
7. The 19th Amendment gave (eighteen-year-olds   women) the right to vote.

B WHICH AMENDMENT?

Write the correct number to complete each sentence.

1. The ___1st___ amendment guarantees people freedom of speech.
2. The _____ amendment established income taxes.
3. The _____ amendment gave women the right to vote.
4. The _____ amendment ended slavery.
5. The _____ amendment gave citizens eighteen years and older the right to vote.
6. The _____ amendment gave African-Americans the right to vote.

C THE 1ST AMENDMENT

These people are all practicing their rights under the 1st Amendment. Match the situation with the 1st Amendment right.

__b__ 1. Cara is a journalist. She's writing a newspaper article about the problems in her community.

____ 2. In our neighborhood we have a church, a mosque, a synagogue, and a temple.

____ 3. Many people are meeting at Riverside Park. They have signs that say "Keep our lakes and rivers clean."

____ 4. Roy is speaking at a town government meeting. He's saying, "Our city isn't safe. We need to hire more police officers."

a. freedom of religion
b. freedom of the press
c. freedom of speech
d. freedom of assembly

Reaching Out!

Work with a small group of students. Compare voting rights in different countries you know. Who can vote? Who can't vote? Make a chart. Present your information to the class.

Voting Around the World

143

A WHEN ARE THEY?

__c__ 1. Thanksgiving is in
____ 2. Christmas is on
____ 3. Halloween is on
____ 4. Independence Day is on
____ 5. Memorial Day is in
____ 6. New Year's Day is on
____ 7. Veterans Day is on
____ 8. Valentine's Day is on
____ 9. Martin Luther King, Jr. Day is in

a. January.
b. July 4th.
c. November.
d. February 14th.
e. October 31st.
f. December 25th.
g. January 1st.
h. November 11th.
i. May.

B HOLIDAY TRADITIONS

1. All the students in our class give cards to each other on ((Valentine's) Veterans) Day.
2. Today is (Independence   New Year's) Day. It's time to put a new calendar on the wall.
3. Every year on (Halloween   Memorial Day) children come to our house and ask for candy.
4. Our family has a big turkey dinner every (Valentine's Day   Thanksgiving).
5. Every year on (Independence   Memorial) Day, there are fireworks in our city.
6. Samira's family doesn't eat until night during their holiday of (Thanksgiving   Ramadan).
7. Americans honor a great man on (Martin Luther King, Jr.   New Year's) Day.
8. We put gifts under the tree on (Halloween   Christmas).

C HOLIDAYS AND THE CALENDAR

Choose the correct answer.

1. Martin Luther King, Jr. Day is always on the third Monday in (June   January).
2. Memorial Day is always on the (first   last) Monday in May.
3. Thanksgiving is always on the fourth (Tuesday   Thursday) in November.

Now look at a calendar for this year and answer the questions.

4. On what date is Martin Luther King, Jr. Day this year? _____
5. On what date is Memorial Day this year? _____
6. On what date is Thanksgiving this year? _____

Reaching Out!

Holidays

What holidays did you celebrate in your country? What holidays do you celebrate now? Compare with a classmate.

The Constitution and the Bill of Rights

The United States Constitution is the supreme law of the land. It established the nation's system of government. The Preamble is the introduction to the Constitution. It begins with three very famous words: We the People.

The Constitution established the three branches of government—legislative, executive, and judicial. The legislative branch makes the laws. It has two parts: the senate and the house of representatives. There are two senators from each state. There are 435 representatives. States with more people have more representatives. For example, California has 53 representatives, but Alaska has only one representative because there aren't many people there. The executive branch enforces the laws. The President is the chief of the executive branch and is also the Commander-in-Chief of the armed forces.

The judicial branch explains the laws. There are nine Supreme Court justices. The chief justice is the head of the Supreme Court.

The people of the United States can change the Constitution. We call these changes amendments. There are 27 amendments to the Constitution. The first ten amendments are called the Bill of Rights. They give rights and freedoms to all people in the United States. The 1st Amendment guarantees freedom of speech, freedom of the press, freedom of religion, and freedom of assembly. Other amendments to the Constitution are also very important. The 13th Amendment ended slavery. The 15th Amendment gave African-Americans the right to vote. The 19th Amendment gave women the right to vote. The 26th Amendment gave citizens eighteen years old and older the right to vote.

1. *We the People* are the first three words of ____.
   a. the Bill of Rights
   b. the 1st Amendment
   c. the Supreme Court
   d. the Preamble to the Constitution

2. The Bill of Rights is ____.
   a. the introduction to the Constitution
   b. the first ten amendments
   c. the first amendment
   d. 27 amendments

3. The Supreme Court ____.
   a. enforces the laws
   b. makes the laws
   c. explains the laws
   d. writes the laws

4. The President is the head of ____.
   a. the Supreme Court
   b. the executive branch
   c. the senate
   d. the house of representatives

5. Each state has ____.
   a. two senators
   b. two representatives
   c. 53 representatives
   d. 435 representatives

6. The ____ gave women the right to vote.
   a. Bill of Rights
   b. 13th Amendment
   c. 15th Amendment
   d. 19th Amendment

WORKBOOK PAGES 1–2

A. INFORMATION ON AN ENVELOPE

1. d	5. g
2. f	6. c
3. a	7. h
4. b	8. e

B. ANITA'S REGISTRATION FORM

REGISTRATION FORM

NAME — FIRST: Anita — MIDDLE INITIAL: K.
LAST: Wilson
MAILING ADDRESS
NUMBER STREET: 17 Elm Street — APT. #: Apt. 3C
CITY: Miami — STATE: FL — ZIP CODE: 33140

D. ALAN'S REGISTRATION FORM

1. d	5. f
2. e	6. a
3. b	7. g
4. c	

WORKBOOK PAGES 3–4

A. ROSA'S FAMILY

1. my mother	4. my brother
2. my sister	5. my grandmother
3. my grandfather	6. my father

B. MALE OR FEMALE?

Male	Female
husband	wife
father	mother
son	daughter
brother	sister
grandfather	grandmother
grandson	granddaughter

Male and Female
parents
children
baby
siblings
grandparents
grandchildren

C. WHO ARE THEY?

1. c	4. a
2. e	5. d
3. b	

D. A FAMILY TREE

1. sister	7. father
2. mother	8. wife
3. son	9. daughter
4. granddaughter	10. brother
5. grandfather	11. parents
6. husband	12. grandmother

WORKBOOK PAGE 5

A. WHO ARE THEY?

a. my brother	f. my nephew
b. my sister-in-law	g. my aunt
c. my niece	h. my uncle
d. my sister	i. my cousin
e. my brother-in-law	

B. GREG AND JULIE'S FAMILY

1. mother	5. nephew
2. mother-in-law	6. nephew
3. brother	7. sister-in-law
4. brother-in-law	8. sister-in-law

WORKBOOK PAGE 6

UNIT 1 READING

1. b	5. c
2. c	6. b
3. b	7. b
4. a	8. a

WORKBOOK PAGE 7

A. THE SUPPLY CLOSET

____	binders	____	pencils
✓	pencil sharpeners	✓	erasers
✓	pens	✓	calculators
✓	rulers	____	chalk
✓	spiral notebooks	____	graph paper
✓	thumbtacks	✓	markers
✓	textbooks	✓	notebook paper
____	workbooks		

B. MARTIN'S DESK

a. printer
b. monitor
c. keyboard
d. mouse
e. workbook
f. graph paper
g. pencil
h. eraser
i. ruler

WORKBOOK PAGE 8

A. TWO CLASSROOMS

Classroom 1
computer
map
table
wastebasket

Classrooms 1 and 2
chairs
desks
teacher's desk
whiteboard

Classroom 2
bookcase
bulletin board
clock
globe

B. YES OR NO?

1. Yes   4. No
2. No   5. Yes
3. Yes

WORKBOOK PAGE 9

A. WHICH ACTION?

1. a   4. a
2. b   5. a
3. a   6. b

B. WHICH WORD?

1. Take   8. Put away
2. Read   9. Go to
3. Write on   10. name
4. Open   11. answer
5. Raise   12. Sit
6. Ask   13. Print
7. board

WORKBOOK PAGE 10

A. WHICH ACTION?

1. a   4. a
2. b   5. b
3. b   6. a

B. DICTIONARY WORK

1. b   4. c
2. d   5. a
3. e

WORKBOOK PAGE 11

A. WHAT'S THE INSTRUCTION?

1. g   5. f
2. e   6. b
3. a   7. h
4. c   8. d

B. WHICH WORD?

1. lights   7. Mark
2. tests   8. Check
3. Take   9. shades
4. Look at   10. questions
5. answers   11. Take out
6. Pass out   12. word

WORKBOOK PAGE 12

A. A PICTURE

1. next to   4. to the left of
2. between   5. behind
3. in front of   6. to the right of

B. THE SUPPLY CLOSET

1. next to   4. between
2. above   5. below
3. to the right of   6. to the left of

WORKBOOK PAGE 13

A. WHERE DO THEY WORK?

1. c   5. f
2. g   6. h
3. e   7. d
4. b   8. a

C. THE LAKEVILLE SCHOOL

1. e   5. b
2. d   6. f
3. c   7. a
4. g   8. h

WORKBOOK PAGE 14

UNIT 2 READING

1. c   5. b
2. b   6. a
3. a   7. b
4. c   8. c

WORKBOOK PAGE 15

A. WHAT'S THE ORDER?

2	4	3
5	2	1
3	1	2
1	5	4
4	3	

WORKBOOK PAGE 16

A. WHICH WORD?

1. Wash   6. cat
2. Do   7. Walk
3. Iron   8. Study
4. Clean   9. Go
5. Go to

WORKBOOK PAGE 17

A. MATCHING

1. b   4. e
2. c   5. f
3. a   6. d

B. SONYA'S FREE TIME

a. watch TV   e. play cards
b. use the computer   f. exercise
c. listen to music   g. play the guitar
d. read the newspaper   h. play basketball

WORKBOOK PAGE 18

A. WHAT ARE THEY SAYING?

1. Good morning.   4. See you later.
2. Fine, thanks.   5. Good night.
3. What's new?   6. How are you?

B. WHICH WORD?

1. thanks   4. evening
2. new   5. soon
3. doing   6. much

WORKBOOK PAGE 19

A. WHAT ARE THEY SAYING?

1. You're welcome.
2. Nice to meet you, too.
3. May I please speak to Mario?
4. Nice to meet you.
5. Sorry. I don't understand.
6. Yes. Hold on a moment.

B. WHICH WORD?

1. ask
2. like
3. again
4. I'm
5. Sorry
6. speak
7. repeat

WORKBOOK PAGE 20

A. WHAT'S THE WEATHER LIKE?

1. sunny
2. cloudy
3. snowing
4. raining
5. windy
6. foggy

B. WHAT'S THE TEMPERATURE?

1. 30°/cold
2. 98°/hot
3. 55°/cool
4. 74°/warm

C. WHICH CITY?

1. Los Angeles
2. Dallas
3. New York
4. Denver
5. Miami

WORKBOOK PAGE 21

UNIT 3 READING

1. c
2. b
3. d
4. c
5. a
6. d
7. b
8. d

WORKBOOK PAGE 22

A. WHAT'S THE NUMBER?

5 five	20 twenty
9 nine	22 twenty-two
3 three	64 sixty-four
14 fourteen	79 seventy-nine
12 twelve	86 eighty-six

93 ninety-three
100 one hundred
112 one hundred twelve
1,000 one thousand
10,000 ten thousand

B. AN IDENTIFICATION CARD

1. c
2. e
3. a
4. b
5. f
6. d

C. COMPLETE THE CLASSROOM INVENTORY

bookcases	3
books	150
calculators	17
chairs	41
desks	39
markers	11
notebooks	28

WORKBOOK PAGE 23

A. WHAT'S THE NUMBER?

1st first
3rd third
7th seventh

12th twelfth
21st twenty-first
40th fortieth

62nd sixty-second
85th eighty-fifth
100th one hundredth

B. WHICH FLOOR?

1. b
2. g
3. e
4. h
5. a
6. c
7. f
8. d

C. WHAT'S THE STREET?

1. 6th
2. 78th
3. 91st
4. 43rd
5. 110th
6. 2nd

WORKBOOK PAGE 24

A. WHAT'S THE TIME?

1.   2.   3.   4.

5.   6.   7.   8.

B. WHICH TIME IS CORRECT?

1. a
2. b
3. a
4. b
5. a
6. a

C. MATCH THE TIMES

1. six ten.
2. half past six.
3. five to seven.
4. ten after seven.
5. a quarter after seven.
6. seven forty-five.

WORKBOOK PAGE 25

A. HOW MUCH IS IT?

1. 50¢ $.50
2. 10¢ $.10
3. 25¢ $.25
4. 1¢ $.01
5. 5¢ $.05
6. $1.00

B. MATCHING: COINS AND AMOUNTS

1. one dollar $1.00
2. one cent $.01
3. fifty cents $.50
4. twenty-five cents $.25
5. five cents   5¢
6. ten cents   10¢

C. WHAT'S THE AMOUNT?

1. $.25
2. $.75
3. $.30
4. $.60
5. $.51
6. $.16

WORKBOOK PAGE 26

A. WHAT'S THE AMOUNT?

1. $6.00
2. $15.00
3. $55.00
4. $22.00
5. $35.00
6. $75.00

B. HOW MUCH IS IT?

1. $4.00
2. $10.00
3. $50.00
4. $60.00
5. $10.25
6. $1.05
7. $20.20
8. $5.03

C. BACK-TO-SCHOOL SALE

$15.90 $4.30 $125.00
$700.00 $2.99 $1.75

WORKBOOK PAGE 27

A. WHICH DAY?

1. Thursday
2. Monday
3. Wednesday
4. Tuesday
5. Sunday
6. Friday

B. MONTHS OF THE YEAR

October	OCT	February	FEB
December	DEC	May	MAY
January	JAN	July	JUL
April	APR	September	SEP

November	NOV
March	MAR
August	AUG
June	JUN

C. DATES

January 25, 2009	1/25/2009
February 18, 2009	2/18/2009
April 13, 2009	4/13/2009
June 22, 2010	6/22/2010

July 14, 2010	7/14/2010
September 5, 2010	9/5/2010
October 20, 2011	10/20/2011
December 31, 2012	12/31/2012

WORKBOOK PAGE 28

A. WHAT'S THE ORDER?

5   4   2
1   3   6

B. WHEN IS IT?

1. b
2. c
3. d
4. a

C. SEASONS

February	Winter	January
October	Fall	November
July	Summer	August
April	Spring	May

D. NINA'S CALENDAR

1. once a week
2. every day
3. twice a week
4. once a week
5. three times a week
6. does the laundry

WORKBOOK PAGE 29

UNIT 4 READING

1. c
2. b
3. d
4. c
5. b
6. a

WORKBOOK PAGE 30

A. AMY'S TAXI

9:00 A.M.	townhouse
10:15 A.M.	dormitory
11:00 A.M.	duplex
12:45 P.M.	apartment building
2:10 P.M.	houseboat
3:30 P.M.	farm

B. WHAT IS IT?

1. duplex
2. nursing home
3. dormitory
4. shelter
5. city
6. ranch
7. mobile home

WORKBOOK PAGE 31

A. WHAT'S THE WORD?

1. sofa
2. loveseat
3. mantel
4. coffee table
5. pillow
6. end table
7. VCR

B. CROSS OUT ONE

1. fireplace screen
2. DVD player
3. drapes
4. magazine holder
5. fireplace

C. GOING SHOPPING

	1st Floor	2nd Floor	3rd Floor	4th Floor
1.			✓	
2.	✓			
3.		✓		
4.				✓
5.			✓	

WORKBOOK PAGE 32

A. IN THE DINING ROOM

1. candlestick
2. spoon
3. tray
4. butter dish
5. sugar bowl
6. plate
7. cup
8. tablecloth

B. THE YARD SALE

- ✓ china cabinet
- ✓ buffet
- ___ dining room chairs
- ___ chandelier
- ✓ teapot
- ✓ coffee pot
- ___ serving dish
- ✓ pitcher
- ✓ sugar bowl
- ✓ mugs
- ✓ glasses
- ___ butter dish
- ✓ salt shaker
- ✓ napkins

C. HOW MUCH IS IT?

glass	$1.00	napkin	25¢
coffee pot	$7.00	buffet	$40.00
platter	$1.50	pitcher	$2.00
china cabinet	$35.00	teapot	$5.00
salt shaker	50¢	mug	75¢

WORKBOOK PAGE 33

A. WHERE ARE THEY?

	On the nightstand	On the dresser	On the bed	On the window
blinds				✓
pillow			✓	
alarm clock	✓			
jewelry box		✓		
curtains				✓
sheet			✓	
clock radio	✓			
blanket			✓	
quilt			✓	

B. TWO BEDROOMS

Bedroom 1
bed frame
blinds
box spring
headboard

Bedrooms 1 & 2
blanket
dresser
lamp
mattress

Bedroom 2
carpet
curtains
mirror
nightstand

WORKBOOK PAGE 34

A. WHERE IN THE KITCHEN?

Counter
canister
dish rack
dishwasher detergent
toaster oven

Wall
cabinet
microwave
potholder
spice rack

Kitchen Table
cookbook
cutting board
food processor
placemat

B. A KITCHEN SALE

tea kettle	$10
cutting board	$17
toaster	$32
potholder	$3
electric mixer	$50
dish rack	$20
dishwashing liquid	$2
coffeemaker	$19
electric can opener	$13
blender	$35

WORKBOOK PAGE 35

A. BABY GIFTS

Rita	car seat
Kathy	baby carriage
Janet	high chair
Gloria	cradle
Claudia	stroller
Flora	mobile

WORKBOOK PAGE 36

A. WHERE ARE THEY?

On the Wall
medicine cabinet
shelf
towel rack

On the Floor
bath mat
bathtub
hamper
plunger
scale
toilet
toilet brush
wastebasket

On the Vanity
electric toothbrush
hair dryer
soap dish
soap dispenser

B. WHAT IS IT?

1. h	6. c
2. f	7. i
3. a	8. e
4. g	9. d
5. b	

C. HOW MUCH IS IT?

$1.75	$1.22	$13.99
$2.99	$23.50	$3.49

WORKBOOK PAGE 37

A. REPAIR TIME!

____ back door
✓ deck
✓ drainpipe
✓ fence
____ gutter
✓ lawn chair
____ patio
✓ screen door
____ side door
✓ tool shed

B. WHICH HOUSE IS FOR SALE?

____ ✓ ____

WORKBOOK PAGE 38

A. A NEW APARTMENT

6	5	8
4	7	2
1		3

B. PEOPLE AND BUILDINGS

People
landlord
building manager
tenant

Parts of a Building
balcony
roof
fire escape

C. APARTMENT ADS

1. b
2. c
3. a
4. b
5. c
6. b

WORKBOOK PAGE 39

A. WHERE ARE THEY?

	In the Lobby	In the Hallway	In the Basement	On the Door
fire alarm		✓		
garbage chute		✓		
intercom	✓			
laundry room			✓	
mailboxes	✓			
peephole				✓
storage locker			✓	

B. WHICH GROUP?

For Fire Safety
fire alarm
smoke detector
sprinkler system

For Security
buzzer
door chain
intercom
lock
peephole
security gate

C. APARTMENT ADS

1. T
2. F
3. T
4. T
5. F
6. F

WORKBOOK PAGE 40

A. THIS HOUSE HAS PROBLEMS!

✓ The roof is leaking.
✓ There are mice.
✓ A sink is clogged.
___ There are ants.
✓ A wall is cracked.
___ The toilet is broken.
✓ There are cockroaches.
___ The refrigerator is broken.
✓ The hot water heater isn't working.

B. WHO CAN FIX IT?

1. c
2. d
3. e
4. b
5. a

C. REPAIRS

1. leaking
2. peeling
3. working
4. sink
5. exterminator
6. termites

WORKBOOK PAGE 41

A. WHAT'S THE WORD?

1. door
2. electrician
3. steps
4. doorbell
5. tiles
6. chimneysweep
7. power

B. WHO CAN FIX IT?

1. c
2. e
3. a
4. b
5. d

C. LOOK IN THE YELLOW PAGES!

1. 305-478-1129
2. 305-478-4693
3. 305-256-9076
4. 305-256-1978
5. 305-478-0591
6. 305-478-4693

WORKBOOK PAGE 42

A. MATCHING SUPPLIES

1. c
2. d
3. b
4. e
5. a

C. FOUR FRIENDS

1. True
2. False
3. True
4. True
5. False
6. True

WORKBOOK PAGE 43

A. JANE'S TOOLBOX

Tools/Hardware	✓	How Many?
bolt		
hammer	✓	2
nail	✓	4
nut	✓	3
pliers	✓	3
saw		
screw		
screwdriver	✓	1
washer	✓	2
wrench	✓	1

C. HOW MUCH IS IT?

1. $7.99
2. $32.94
3. $2.98
4. $9.97
5. $45.00
6. $2.49
7. $15.80
8. $2.87

WORKBOOK PAGE 44

UNIT 5 READING

1. c   4. b
2. d   5. d
3. c   6. a

WORKBOOK PAGE 45

A. SHOPPING IN CENTERVILLE

1. City Bank
2. Sunshine Coffee Shop
3. West Street Clinic
4. Tech World Computer Store
5. Harper's Book Store
6. Little Friends Day-Care Center
7. Henry's Barber Shop
8. Centerville Bus Station
9. Day & Night Convenience Store

WORKBOOK PAGE 46

A. WHAT'S THE PLACE?

1. hair salon
2. fast-food restaurant
3. furniture store
4. electronics store
5. department store
6. florist
7. service station, North
8. grocery store, Seventh
9. drug store, Sixth

WORKBOOK PAGE 47

A. SHOPPING AT THE MALL

1. 8   8. 2
2. 13   9. 10
3. 4   10. 1
4. 9   11. 5
5. 7   12. 12
6. 3   13. 6
7. 11

WORKBOOK PAGE 48

A. WHAT'S THE PLACE?

1. post office
2. pet shop
3. video store
4. pizza shop, restaurant
5. toy store
6. supermarket
7. shoe store, First
8. shopping mall, River

WORKBOOK PAGE 49

A. PEOPLE, TRANSPORTATION, AND BUILDINGS

People
taxi driver
meter maid

Transportation
taxi/cab
garbage truck
subway

Buildings
courthouse
city hall
police station
jail

B. WHERE IS IT?

1. police station   4. courthouse
2. parking lot   5. trash container
3. sidewalk   6. fire alarm box

C. SPRINGVILLE'S BUDGET

sewers	$20,000
parking meters	$30,000
parking lots	$40,000
sidewalks	$50,000
courthouse	$60,000
street lights	$90,000
fire hydrants	$100,000

WORKBOOK PAGE 50

A. PEOPLE, TRANSPORTATION, AND BUILDINGS

People
bus driver
pedestrian
street vendor

Transportation
bus stop
ice cream truck
motorcycle

Buildings
fire station
newsstand
parking garage

B. TRUE OR FALSE?

1. T   5. F
2. F   6. T
3. T   7. T
4. F

WORKBOOK PAGE 51

UNIT 6 READING

1. d   5. b
2. c   6. a
3. a   7. b
4. d   8. c

WORKBOOK PAGE 52

A. GROUPING WORDS

Age
middle-aged
old
young

Weight
average weight
heavy
slim
thin

Height
average height
short
tall

B. WHAT'S THE ORDER?

2	3	1			
3	1	2			
4	3	6	1	5	2

C. MOTHER AND DAUGHTER

Mother
middle-aged
short

Both
thin

Daughter
young
tall

WORKBOOK PAGE 53

A. OUR CLASS

1. long	4. mustache
2. curly	5. wavy
3. black	6. shoulder length

B. FAMILY PHOTOGRAPHS

1. Fred	3. Gary
2. Nick	4. Alan

C. FATHER AND SON

Father
beard
short hair
thin

Both
blond hair
straight hair

Son
heavy
long hair
mustache

WORKBOOK PAGE 54

A. OPPOSITES

1. c	6. i
2. e	7. h
3. d	8. j
4. b	9. f
5. a	10. g

B. SAME OR OPPOSITE?

1. O	5. S
2. S	6. O
3. O	7. O
4. S	8. S

C. WHICH WORD DOESN'T BELONG?

1. c	5. a
2. a	6. c
3. b	7. b
4. b	

WORKBOOK PAGE 55

A. OPPOSITES

1. d	5. h
2. a	6. g
3. c	7. e
4. b	8. f

B. SAME OR OPPOSITE?

1. O	4. S
2. S	5. O
3. O	6. S

WORKBOOK PAGE 56

A. WHICH GROUP?

annoyed	exhausted
unhappy	sleepy
upset	tired

B. PROBLEMS

1. c	4. e
2. d	5. b
3. a	

WORKBOOK PAGE 57

A. HOW DO THEY FEEL?

1. Lonely	4. Afraid
2. Bored	5. Homesick
3. Jealous	6. Frustrated

WORKBOOK PAGE 58

UNIT 7 READING

1. c	5. b
2. b	6. a
3. c	7. d
4. d	8. a

WORKBOOK PAGE 59

A. HOW MUCH IS IT?

Fruit	Price
grapefruit	$1.79
banana	$.35
pear	$.80
watermelon	$4.00

Fruit	Price
pineapple	$3.75
orange	$.60
lemon	$.45
apple	$.50

B. THEY GO TOGETHER

1. d	5. g
2. c	6. h
3. b	7. f
4. a	8. e

C. LINDA'S FRUIT SALAD

My Shopping List
1 banana
1 coconut
2 mangoes
2 pears

WORKBOOK PAGE 60

A. HOW LONG CAN YOU KEEP THEM?

1. True
2. False
3. True
4. False
5. True
6. False

B. FIND THE RECEIPT

_____ _____ ✓

WORKBOOK PAGE 61

A. WHICH DOESN'T BELONG?

1. b
2. c
3. b
4. a
5. c
6. b
7. c

B. LOOK AT THE RECEIPTS

1. a
2. d
3. c
4. d
5. a
6. c
7. b
8. c

WORKBOOK PAGE 62

B. DAIRY PRODUCTS AND FAT

1. _____   3. ✓   5. _____
   ✓   _____   ✓
2. _____   4. ✓   6. ✓
   ✓   _____   _____

C. COUNTING CALORIES

1. _____   3. _____   5. ✓
   ✓   ✓   _____
2. ✓   4. _____   6. _____
   _____   ✓   ✓

WORKBOOK PAGE 63

A. WHICH GROUP?

Meat and Poultry
bologna
ham
roast beef
turkey

Cheese
American cheese
cheddar cheese
mozzarella
Swiss cheese

Snack Foods
nuts
popcorn
potato chips
pretzels

WORKBOOK PAGE 64

A. FIX THE SIGNS!

Packaged Goods
~~mayonnaise~~

Baking Products
~~pickles~~

Canned Goods
~~mustard~~

Condiments
~~cookies~~

Baked Goods
~~salt~~

B. WHICH AISLE?

bread	4
cake	4
cake mix	5
canned fruit	1
cereal	2
crackers	2
English muffins	4
flour	5
ketchup	3
mustard	3
noodles	2
olive oil	3
pepper	3
relish	3
rice	2
salt	3
soup	1
spaghetti	2
spices	3
sugar	5
tuna fish	1

C. SHOPPING WITH COUPONS

Food	Aisle	Save
cereal	2	25¢
soup	1	35¢
bread	4	30¢
ketchup	3	40¢

WORKBOOK PAGE 65

A. WHICH DOESN'T BELONG?

1. b
2. a
3. b
4. c
5. b

B. AMY LEE'S PANTRY

Item	Has	Needs
baby cereal		✓
baby food	✓	
diapers	✓	
dog food		✓
liquid soap	✓	
napkins		✓
paper cups	✓	
paper towels	✓	
sandwich bags	✓	
soap		✓
tissues	✓	
trash bags	✓	

WORKBOOK PAGE 66

A. HOW MANY?

2	4	3
3	3	8

B. GROUPING WORDS

People
bagger
cashier
clerk
manager
shopper

Parts of a Store
aisle
can-return machine
checkout line
scale

WORKBOOK PAGE 67

A. WHAT'S THE CONTAINER?

Can
coffee
tuna fish

Box
cereal
tissues

Jar
baby food
mayonnaise

Roll
paper towels
toilet paper

Bunch
bananas
grapes

Half-Gallon
ice cream
milk

Package
pita bread
rolls

Pound
beef
butter

Head
cabbage
lettuce

B. RECYCLING IN WESTON

✓	✓	x	✓	✓
x	✓	✓	✓	x

WORKBOOK PAGE 68

A. ABBREVIATIONS

1. c
2. e
3. b
4. f
5. a
6. d

B. FROM SMALL TO BIG

2	5
4	3
1	6

C. MATCHING MEASUREMENTS

1. 1 fluid ounce
2. 8 fluid ounces
3. 32 fluid ounces
4. 16 fluid ounces
5. 128 fluid ounces

D. WHAT'S THE WORD?

1. teaspoons
2. cups
3. pints
4. quarts

E. TWO RECIPES

Ingredient	Rita uses	Ron uses
vinegar	3 tablespoons	4 tablespoons
mustard	1 tablespoon	--------------
sugar	1 teaspoon	--------------
olive oil	6 fluid ounces	1 cup
garlic	--------------	1 teaspoon
onions	--------------	2 teaspoons

WORKBOOK PAGE 69

A. MATCHING MEASUREMENTS

1. 4 ounces
2. 8 ounces
3. 12 ounces
4. 16 ounces

B. MATCHING WITH ABBREVIATIONS

1. b
2. c
3. d
4. a

C. WHAT'S IN THE CONTAINERS?

1. d
2. a
3. b
4. e
5. f
6. c

D. COMPARE THE RECIPES

Who Uses More?	Marco	Jane
kidney beans		✓
salt		✓
carrots	✓	
olive oil		✓
ground beef	✓	
jalapeño peppers	✓	
tomatoes	✓	
onions		✓

WORKBOOK PAGE 70

A. PREPARING THE CHILI

3	4	2
6	1	5

B. WHICH DOESN'T BELONG?

1. b
2. a
3. c
4. b
5. a

WORKBOOK PAGE 71

A. INGREDIENTS

1. f   5. g
2. c   6. b
3. a   7. d
4. e

B. FOOD, CONDIMENT, OR PAPER?

	Food	Condiment	Paper
relish		✓	
frozen yogurt	✓		
mustard		✓	
straws			✓
mayonnaise		✓	
hot dog	✓		
lids			✓

C. NUTRITIONAL INFORMATION

1. T   6. T
2. F   7. F
3. T   8. F
4. F   9. T
5. F

WORKBOOK PAGE 72

A. THE SUNLIGHT CAFE

waffles	$3.50
coffee	$1.25
toast	99¢
donut	85¢
milk	$1.25

egg salad sandwich	$2.75
hot chocolate	$1.25
ham and cheese sandwich	$4.00
tea	$1.25
muffin	$1.50

WORKBOOK PAGE 73

A. WHICH GROUP?

People in a Restaurant
busperson
chef
diner
host
server
waitress

Things in a Restaurant
booster seat
booth
bread basket
dining room
menu
salad bar

B. WHAT DO THEY DO?

1. seats the customers
2. eats the meal
3. takes the order
4. pours the water
5. prepares the meal

D. WHAT ARE THEY DOING?

1. d   5. e
2. f   6. g
3. c   7. a
4. b

WORKBOOK PAGE 74

A. WHICH GROUP?

Dishes
bread-and-butter plate
cup
dinner plate
salad plate
saucer
soup bowl

Silverware
butter knife
dinner fork
knife
salad fork
soup spoon
teaspoon

B. HOW TO SET A TABLE

1. forks   5. wine glass
2. dinner plate   6. salad plate
3. dinner fork   7. water glass
4. saucer

C. WHAT'S THE ORDER?

4   5
1   2
6   7
3   8

WORKBOOK PAGE 75

A. NINA'S FAMILY RESTAURANT

Appetizers   Side Dishes
Salads   Desserts
Entrees

B. ON THE MENU

antipasto	
apple pie	✓
baked chicken	✓
baked potato	✓
broiled fish	✓
chicken wings	
chocolate cake	✓
fruit cup	✓
Greek salad	✓
ice cream	✓
jello	✓
mashed potatoes	
meatloaf	✓
mixed vegetables	✓
noodles	
rice	✓
roast beef	✓
shrimp cocktail	
tomato juice	✓
tossed salad	✓

C. THE RESTAURANT BILL

Nina's Family Restaurant	
tomato juice	$2.00
tossed salad	$3.00
roast beef	$8.95
baked potato	$1.95
mixed vegetables	$3.95
apple pie	$2.75
Total:	$22.60

Nina's Family Restaurant	
nachos	$5.25
Greek salad	$3.75
baked chicken	$7.95
broiled fish	$8.50
rice	$1.50
french fries	$1.75
chocolate cake	$2.95
Total:	$31.65

WORKBOOK PAGE 76

UNIT 8 READING

1. a
2. c
3. b
4. c
5. d
6. a

WORKBOOK PAGE 77

A. WHAT COLOR ARE THEY?

1. yellow
2. green
3. beige
4. green
5. brown and green
6. pink
7. blue
8. purple
9. yellow
10. blue

C. COLORS AND CARS

Color	Number of Cars
black	160
blue	100
green	40
red	50
silver	120
white	170

WORKBOOK PAGE 78

A. WHAT ARE THEY WEARING?

1. skirt
2. vest
3. jacket
4. suit
5. shorts

B. A CLOTHING SALE

Clothing	Price
dresses	$65
blouses	$35
shorts	$25
shirts	$40
three-piece suits	$250
T-shirts	$16
sweaters	$50
overalls	$65
pants	$29
ties	$30

C. DRESS CODE

1. Yes
2. No
3. No
4. Yes
5. Yes

WORKBOOK PAGE 79

A. WHAT ARE THEY WEARING?

1. coat
2. scarf
3. cap
4. trench coat
5. down vest

B. WHAT ARE PEOPLE WEARING?

Miami
trench coats
ponchos
rain boots
rain hats

New York
gloves
ear muffs
overcoats
mittens

C. OUTERWEAR SALE

Clothing Item	Regular Price	Sale Price
boots	$30	$18
caps	$14	$6
ear muffs	$8	$5
gloves	$22	$15
mittens	$18	$12
umbrellas	$12	$8

WORKBOOK PAGE 80

A. WHICH DEPARTMENT?

Sleepwear
bathrobe, nightgown, nightshirt, pajamas

Men's Underwear
boxer shorts, briefs, jockstrap, undershirt

Women's Underwear
bra, panties, pantyhose, slip

B. WHO WEARS THESE?

Men
boxer shorts
jockstrap

Men and Women
bathrobe
long underwear
pajamas
slippers

Women
bra
camisole
nightgown
slip

C. HOW MUCH WILL THEY SPEND?

1. $20	3. $34
2. $49	4. $55

WORKBOOK PAGE 81

A. WHAT ARE THEY WEARING?

1. sweatpants	5. jogging
2. running	6. high heels
3. cover-up	7. thongs
4. tank top	8. running shoes

WORKBOOK PAGE 82

A. WHICH ITEM?

1. bracelet	5. backpack
2. ring	6. briefcase
3. wallet	7. pearls
4. change	

B. WHERE DO YOU KEEP THEM?

1. b	4. e
2. d	5. c
3. a	

C. WHAT'S IN THE STORE?

Jewelry Items	Prices
pin	$250
bracelet	$300
ring	$700
earrings	$150
locket	$500
pearls	$800
cuff links	$350
watch	$200
chain	$100

WORKBOOK PAGE 83

A. WHICH ONE DOESN'T BELONG?

1. b	4. a
2. c	5. c
3. b	

B. COMPLETE THE STORE TAGS

1. striped, extra-large	3. short-sleeved, small
2. solid white, medium	4. plaid, large

WORKBOOK PAGE 84

A. FIND THE OPPOSITE

1. too narrow	4. too low
2. too light	5. too baggy
3. too plain	

B. HOW CAN I FIX IT?

1. Let it out.	4. Take it in.
2. Shorten it.	5. Clean it.
3. Lengthen it.	

C. SAM'S BARGAIN BASEMENT

1. missing button	3. stained collar
2. ripped pocket	4. broken zipper

D. RETURNING CLOTHES

RAY'S DEPARTMENT STORE RETURNS		December 15
ITEM	**REASON FOR RETURN**	
Shoes:	The heels are too __high__ .	
Shirt:	The collar is __ripped__ .	
Jacket:	The sleeve is __stained__ .	
Sweater:	The sleeves are too __long__ .	
Pants:	They're too __baggy__ .	

WORKBOOK PAGE 85

A. WHICH DEPARTMENT?

Electronics Department	television
Jewelry Counter	earrings
Furniture Department	sofa
Women's Clothing Department	skirt
Household Appliances Department	refrigerator
Snack Bar	hamburger
Men's Clothing Department	tie
Housewares Department	blender

B. THE STORE DIRECTORY

1. 1	7. 5
2. 4	8. 3
3. 5	9. 1
4. 3	10. 2
5. 5	11. 4
6. 1	

WORKBOOK PAGE 86

A. WHICH IS FIRST?

1. b	4. a
2. a	5. b
3. b	6. b

B. WHERE CAN YOU FIND THEM?

1. sale sign	3. size, label
2. price tag	4. total price, receipt

C. WHAT'S ON THE RECEIPT?

1. c
2. a
3. d
4. e
5. b

6. $24.50
7. $35.00
8. $1.23
9. $25.73
10. -$10.50

WORKBOOK PAGE 87

A. VIDEO OR AUDIO?

	Video	Audio
1.		✓
2.	✓	
3.		✓
4.		✓
5.		✓
6.	✓	
7.		✓
8.	✓	

B. MATCHING EQUIPMENT

1. c
2. d
3. b
4. a
5. h
6. g
7. e
8. f

C. A BIG SALE!

Item	Price
cell phone	$79
camera	$400
answering machine	$28
flash	$50

Item	Price
radio	$22
boombox	$33
camcorder	$395
TV	$289

WORKBOOK PAGE 88

A. WHICH COMPUTER ITEMS?

1. CD-ROM drive
2. screen
3. keyboard
4. track ball
5. printer
6. computer game
7. notebook computer

B. SHOPPING AT TECH-CITY COMPUTERS

Item	Graciela	Ahmed	Lin
CPU	✓		
monitor	✓		
scanner		✓	
mouse			✓
notebook computer		✓	
printer	✓		
word-processing program			✓
modem		✓	

WORKBOOK PAGE 89

UNIT 9 READING

1. b
2. d
3. c
4. d
5. a
6. b

WORKBOOK PAGE 90

A. MAKE A DEPOSIT

B. MAKE A WITHDRAWAL

C. WRITE A CHECK

D. WHAT DO I USE?

1. b
2. e
3. a
4. c
5. d

WORKBOOK PAGE 91

A. USING AN ATM

3
5
2
6
1
4

C. HOUSEHOLD BILLS

$44.82 $45.30 $625.00
$60.00 $200.00 $74.00

D. PAY THE BILL

276
DATE _____
PAY TO THE ORDER OF Horizon Telephone Company $ 53.42
Fifty-three dollars and 42/100 _____ Dollars
ANB American National Bank
For _____   _____
⑈746599331⑈88823422⑈276⑈

WORKBOOK PAGE 92

A. POSTAL RATES

stamp	42¢
sheet of stamps	$8.40
roll of stamps	$42
air letter	90¢
book of stamps	$8.40
postcard	27¢

B. INFORMATION ON AN ENVELOPE

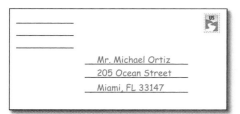

return address ←
stamp
mailing address
zip code

Emily Chang
225 Jefferson St.
Austin, TX 78705

Ivan Markov
2192 River Ave.
Santa Barbara, CA 93101

C. ADDRESSING AN ENVELOPE

Mr. Michael Ortiz
205 Ocean Street
Miami, FL 33147

WORKBOOK PAGE 93

A. WHERE CAN YOU FIND THESE?

Item	Periodical Section	Media Section	Reference Section
atlases			✓
books on tape		✓	
CDs		✓	
computer software		✓	
dictionaries			✓

Item	Periodical Section	Media Section	Reference Section
DVDs		✓	
encyclopedias			✓
magazines	✓		
newspapers	✓		
videotapes		✓	

B. BORROWING FROM THE MIDVILLE LIBRARY

1. Yes
2. No
3. Yes
4. No
5. Yes
6. No

C. WHERE ARE THEY?

1. Media, 2
2. Foreign Language, 3
3. Reference, 1
4. Children's, 2
5. Periodical, 1

WORKBOOK PAGE 94

A. WHAT NUMBER DO YOU CALL?

1. c
2. e
3. a
4. f
5. d
6. b

C. WHAT DOES WATERVILLE NEED?

1. nursery
2. sanitation workers
3. emergency room
4. eldercare workers
5. police officers
6. gym

WORKBOOK PAGE 95

UNIT 10 READING

1. a
2. d
3. c
4. b
5. c
6. b

WORKBOOK PAGE 96

A. WHICH WORD DOESN'T BELONG?

1. c
2. b
3. a
4. b
5. c
6. b
7. c
8. a

B. WHAT IS IT?

1. shoulder
2. thigh
3. eyelid
4. tooth
5. forehead
6. chest

C. WHERE DOES IT HURT?

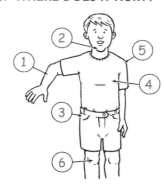

WORKBOOK PAGE 97

A. WHAT'S THE MATTER?

1. foot
2. throat
3. hand
4. spinal column
5. stomach
6. lungs

B. WHAT PART OF THE BODY IS IT?

1. heart
2. wrist
3. heel
4. knuckle
5. brain
6. gallbladder
7. palm

C. WHERE ARE THEY?

skull
ribcage
pelvis
ankle
brain
throat
lungs
stomach

WORKBOOK PAGE 98

A. THE FLU

1. sore throat
2. runny nose
3. four
4. chest pains
5. high temperature
6. winter

WORKBOOOK PAGE 99

A. WHAT HAPPENED TO THEM?

1. sprained
2. broke
3. scraped
4. bruised
5. twisted
6. burned

C. WHY TELCO'S EMPLOYEES ARE MISSING WORK

	Colds and Fevers	Stomach Ailments	Injuries
1.			✓
2.	✓		
3.		✓	
4.			✓
5.		✓	
6.	✓		
7.		✓	
8.			✓

WORKBOOK PAGE 100

A. FIRST-AID KIT

1. f
2. d
3. g
4. e
5. i
6. a
7. j
8. b
9. c
10. h

B. WHAT CAN THEY USE?

1. c
2. d
3. a
4. e
5. b

C. WHAT'S THE REMEDY?

1. c
2. e
3. d
4. a
5. b

WORKBOOK PAGES 101–102

A. EMERGENCY OR ILLNESS?

Medical Emergencies
allergic reaction
frostbite
heart attack
overdose on drugs

Illnesses
AIDS
cancer
diabetes
measles

C. VACCINATION GUIDE

1. b
2. a
3. b
4. c
5. a

D. ARE THEY CONTAGIOUS?

Illness	Contagious	Not Contagious
asthma		✓
cancer		✓
diabetes		✓
high blood pressure		✓
influenza	✓	
measles	✓	
mumps	✓	
strep throat	✓	

WORKBOOK PAGE 103

A. WHAT ARE THEY GOING TO USE?

1. thermometer
2. stethoscope
3. eye chart
4. scale
5. gauge
6. needle

C. WHAT ARE THEY DOING?

1. d
2. e
3. b
4. a
5. f
6. c

WORKBOOK PAGE 104

A. MATCHING

1. d
2. a
3. e
4. c
5. b

B. DOCTOR, DENTIST, OR BOTH?

1. B
2. DE
3. B
4. DO
5. B
6. B
7. DE
8. DE
9. DO
10. DE
11. DO
12. B

C. WHEN DOES IT HAPPEN?

4	5
6	2
1	3

WORKBOOK PAGE 105

A. MATCHING

1. e
2. d
3. f
4. b
5. a
6. c

B. FIND THE ANSWER!

1. exercising
2. resting
3. braces
4. ear
5. fluids
6. walker
7. wheelchair
8. physical therapy

WORKBOOK PAGE 106

A. AILMENTS AND MEDICINE

1. f
2. c
3. d
4. h
5. g
6. e
7. b
8. a

B. WHAT'S THE DOSAGE?

1. B
2. D
3. C
4. F
5. A
6. E

C. FOLLOW THE INSTRUCTIONS

1. c
2. a
3. b
4. e
5. d
6. f

WORKBOOK PAGE 107

A. IN A PATIENT'S ROOM

1. d
2. f
3. g
4. a
5. c
6. e
7. h
8. b

B. PERSON, PLACE, OR THING?

T	T	PER
T	PL	PER
PL	PER	PER

C. WHERE IN THE HOSPITAL?

Person	Floor
surgeon	3
EMT	1
nurse	5
lab technician	4
obstetrician	2
X-ray technician	6
anesthesiologist	3

WORKBOOK PAGE 108

A. WHICH PRODUCT?

1. a toothbrush
2. shampoo
3. razor
4. nail clipper
5. mouthwash
6. bubble bath
7. mascara

B. WHICH WORD DOESN'T BELONG?

1. conditioner
2. shower cap
3. scissors
4. sunscreen
5. nail polish
6. blush

C. PERSONAL HYGIENE TIPS

1. soap
2. bath
3. shampoo
4. comb
5. clipper
6. floss
7. mouthwash

WORKBOOK PAGE 109

A. WHAT DO YOU USE TO . . . ?

Feed the Baby
bib
bottle
formula
nipple

Change the Baby
baby powder
diaper pins
ointment
training pants
wipes

Bathe the Baby
baby lotion
baby shampoo
cotton swabs

B. BABYSITTING

1. d
2. e
3. b
4. c
5. a

C. NEWBORN BABY INVENTORY

Items Ramona has:
baby lotion
baby powder
cotton swabs
diaper pins
pacifier

Shopping List
baby shampoo
diapers
ointment
wipes

WORKBOOK PAGE 110

UNIT 11 READING

1. d   4. b
2. b   5. a
3. c   6. d

WORKBOOK PAGE 111

A. WHICH SUBJECT?

1. art
2. home economics
3. chemistry
4. health
5. geography
6. physical education
7. French

B. CLASS SCHEDULES

1. math
2. history
3. chemistry
4. physics
5. business education
6. English
7. geography
8. computer science
9. biology

WORKBOOK PAGE 112

A. WHAT KIND OF ACTIVITY?

Music
band
choir
orchestra

Writing
literary magazine
school newspaper
yearbook

Clubs
chess
computer
international

B. WHICH ACTIVITY?

1. choir
2. school newspaper
3. orchestra
4. yearbook
5. community service

C. THE JEFFERSON HIGH SCHOOL YEARBOOK

Amy
choir
pep squad
yearbook

Amy and Jenny
international club
drama
debate club

Jenny
band
computer club
student government

WORKBOOK PAGE 113

A. ARITHMETIC CHART

	Addition	Subtraction	Multiplication	Division
1.			✓	
2.	✓			
3.				✓
4.		✓		
5.	✓			
6.			✓	
7.		✓		
8.				✓

B. ARITHMETIC SIGNS AND WORDS

1. __−__, minus
2. __×__, times
3. __+__, plus
4. __÷__, divided by

C. ON SALE!

1. 3/4
2. 1/3
3. 2/3
4. 1/4
5. 1/2

WORKBOOK PAGE 114

A. WHICH ONE DOESN'T BELONG?

1. b
2. c
3. a
4. b
5. c

B. WHICH SHAPES?

1. A
2. C
3. B
4. B
5. A
6. A
7. C
8. B
9. B
10. A

C. ABBREVIATIONS

1. inch
2. foot
3. inches
4. feet

D. AMANDA'S LIVING ROOM

1. 14 feet
2. 16 feet
3. 7 feet
4. 4 feet
5. 3 feet
6. 5 feet
7. 57 inches
8. 36 inches
9. 39 inches

WORKBOOK PAGE 115

A. PARTS OF SPEECH

1. verbs
2. articles
3. prepositions
4. pronouns
5. nouns
6. adjectives

B. MISSING PUNCTUATION

1. h
2. d
3. a
4. c
5. g
6. f
7. b
8. e

C. HOW TO WRITE A COMPOSITION

1. brainstorm
2. ideas
3. draft
4. title
5. paragraphs
6. feedback
7. corrections
8. final
9. period
10. exclamation point
11. question mark

WORKBOOK PAGE 116

A. WHICH ONE DOESN'T BELONG?

1. biography
2. invitation
3. postcard
4. short story
5. memo
6. instant message

B. MATCHING

1. c
2. a
3. f
4. b
5. d
6. e

WORKBOOK PAGE 117

A. LAND OR WATER?

Land
canyon
desert
island
meadow
peninsula
plains

Water
bay
lake
ocean
pond
river
stream

B. WHERE ARE THEY?

1. meadow
2. plateau
3. desert
4. rainforest
5. an island
6. lake

C. WHAT'S ON THE MAP?

1. mountain
2. river
3. lake
4. seashore
5. ocean
6. bay
7. peninsula
8. island

WORKBOOK PAGE 118

A. NEW SCIENCE EQUIPMENT

Equipment to Order	
12 test tubes	$7.00
12 flasks	$21.50
12 beakers	$22.00
12 funnels	$20.00
12 graduated cylinders	$45.00
24 Petri dishes	$40.00

B. WHAT ARE THEY USING?

1. microscope
2. a prism
3. dropper
4. crucible tongs
5. Bunsen burner
6. funnel
7. balance

C. THE SCIENTIFIC METHOD

6
1
5
3
2
4

D. SCIENCE EQUIPMENT

___	balance	✓	test tube
✓	beaker	___	forceps
___	magnet	✓	funnel
✓	prism	✓	dropper
___	scale	✓	Petri dish
✓	flask	___	Bunsen burner

WORKBOOK PAGE 119

UNIT 12 READING

1. b
2. c
3. b
4. d
5. a
6. d

WORKBOOK PAGE 120

A. WHAT DO THEY DO?

They work with food.
baker
butcher
chef

They build things.
bricklayer
carpenter
construction worker

They work in an office.
accountant
businessman
computer software engineer

B. JOB OPENINGS

Actor   Butcher   Barber
Chef   Carpenter   Baker

C. FROM HIGH TO LOW

1 accountant
2 actor
3 artist
7 barber

4 carpenter
8 cashier
6 construction worker
5 cook

WORKBOOK PAGE 121

A. WHERE DO THEY WORK?

They work indoors.
custodian
data entry clerk
factory worker
food-service worker
garment worker
hairdresser

They work outdoors.
dockworker
farmer
fisher
landscaper

B. THE RIGHT JOB

1. data entry clerk
2. health-care aide
3. foreman
4. landscaper
5. custodian
6. delivery person
7. homemaker
8. dockworker
9. garment worker

C. JOBS IN THE FUTURE

Yes   No
No   Yes
Yes   Yes

WORKBOOK PAGE 122

A. THE RIGHT JOB

1. manager
2. receptionist
3. physician assistant
4. pilot
5. housekeeper
6. mechanic

B. JOB OPENINGS

Manicurist   Housekeeper   Mechanic
Medical Assistant   Machine Operator   Pilot

C. FUTURE JOBS

pilot	5	lawyer	6
mechanic	3	manager	2
police officer	4	photographer	7

WORKBOOK PAGE 123

A. WHAT'S THE OCCUPATION?

1. secretary
2. supervisor
3. teacher
4. stock clerk
5. server

B. GETTING A LICENSE

$35	$80	X	$100
$70	X	$110	X

C. JOB OPENINGS AT THE MID-CITY MALL

1. tailor
2. server
3. salesperson/stock clerk
4. stock clerk/salesperson
5. secretary
6. instructor

WORKBOOK PAGE 124

A. WHAT DO THEY DO?

1. guard buildings.
2. draw.
3. grow vegetables.
4. file.
5. build things.
6. clean.
7. fly airplanes.
8. mow lawns.
9. cook.
10. assist patients.

C. WHAT ARE THEIR SKILLS?

draw
cook
file
mow lawns
grow vegetables
build things
operate equipment
drive a truck
fly an airplane

WORKBOOK PAGE 125

A. WHAT DO THEY DO?

1. use a cash register.
2. wash dishes.
3. take inventory.
4. serve food.
5. sew.
6. take care of elderly people.
7. supervise people.
8. type.
9. translate.
10. fix things.

B. WHAT JOB SHOULD THEY APPLY FOR?

1. waiter, River Restaurant
2. instructor, Ace Language School
3. cashier, Sam's Appliances
4. health-care attendant, Oakville Nursing Home
5. repairperson, Sam's Appliances
6. cook, River Restaurant
7. secretary, Ace Language School

WORKBOOK PAGE 126

A. WHAT'S THE ABBREVIATION?

1. part-time
2. full-time
3. hour
4. previous
5. experience
6. required
7. evenings
8. available
9. Monday
10. Friday
11. excellent

B. TRUE OR FALSE?

1. F
2. T
3. F
4. T
5. F
6. F
7. T
8. T

C. JOB SEARCH TIPS

1. ad
2. resume
3. application
4. Dress
5. experience/skills
6. skills/experience
7. salary/benefits
8. benefits/salary
9. note

WORKBOOK PAGE 127

A. HOW MANY?

2	2
3	3
2	14

B. WHERE IN THE FACTORY?

1. loading dock.
2. work stations.
3. warehouse.
4. conveyor belt.
5. warehouse.
6. union notices.

C. PERSON, PLACE, OR THING?

Things in the Factory
conveyor belt
hand truck
suggestion box
time clock

Places in the Factory
loading dock
payroll office
shipping department
warehouse

People in the Factory
factory worker
line supervisor
packer
shipping clerk

A. AT THE CONSTRUCTION SITE

1. wheelbarrow
2. toolbelt
3. cement mixer
4. trowel
5. crane
6. pipes
7. tape measure

B. COMPARING CONSTRUCTION SITES

Site 1
blueprints
front-end loader
lumber

Sites 1 & 2
bricks
dump truck
pipes

Site 2
jackhammer
tape measure
wheelbarrow

A. WHAT DO THEY PROTECT?

1. earplugs, ears, safety earmuffs
2. goggles, eyes, safety glasses
3. safety boots, feet, toe guards
4. hard hat, head, helmet
5. safety vest, body, back support
6. respirator, nose and mouth, mask

B. WARNING SIGNS

B	A	F	C
E	H	D	G

C. WHICH WORKPLACE IS SAFER?

The Ajax Company				✓
The Bay Company	✓	✓	✓	

UNIT 13 READING

1. b
2. d
3. c
4. b
5. c
6. a

A. WHICH GROUP?

Forms of Transportation
bus
cab
subway
train

People
bus driver
conductor
passenger
taxi driver

Places to Wait
bus stop
platform
taxi stand

You Pay with These
fare card
ticket
token

B. GOING PLACES

1. platform
2. conductor
3. bus stop
4. fare card
5. transfer
6. bus route

C. A CITY BUS

1. T
2. F
3. T
4. F
5. F

A. OPPOSITE PREPOSITIONS

1. e
2. c
3. a
4. b
5. d

C. TRAVELING

1. up
2. over
3. around
4. through
5. onto
6. down
7. off

D. HOW DONNA GETS TO WORK

✓
___
___
✓
___
___

A. GETTING A DRIVER'S LICENSE

C	F	B	H
G	A	D	E

C. DRIVING DIRECTIONS

WORKBOOK PAGE 134

A. AT THE AIRPORT

1. d
2. a
3. g
4. f
5. b
6. c
7. e

B. AIRPORT SIGNS AND MONITORS

2	18	1:25
3	16	2:30
2	23B	2:20
3	29	2:15

C. WHICH WORD?

1. ticket
2. carry-on bag
3. luggage carrier
4. Gate 41

WORKBOOK PAGE 135

UNIT 14 READING

1. d
2. b
3. c
4. a
5. b
6. c

WORKBOOK PAGE 136

A. THE WRONG PLACE!

1. yard sale
2. planetarium
3. play
4. flea market
5. movies

B. A GUIDE TO OAKDALE

1. F
2. F
3. T
4. T
5. F
6. F
7. T

WORKBOOK PAGE 137

A. INDOORS OR OUTDOORS?

Indoor Activities
billiards
bowling
boxing
ping pong
racquetball
weightlifting

Outdoor Activities
badminton
biking
golf
horseback riding
rollerblading
tennis

B. ON THE BALL!

bowling
golf
ping pong
racquetball
tennis

C. WHAT CAN YOU DO?

1. T
2. F
3. F
4. T
5. F
6. T

WORKBOOK PAGE 138

A. WHICH GROUP?

Court
basketball
volleyball

Field
baseball
football
lacrosse
soccer

Rink
hockey

B. CLASS SURVEY

| 4 | 6 | 10 |
| 2 | 8 | 9 |

WORKBOOK PAGE 139

A. FIND THE TICKETS

| $40.00 | $50.00 |
| $30.00 | $70.00 |

B. WHICH GROUP?

Kinds of Music
classical
country
hip hop
jazz
rock

Kinds of Movies
adventure
cartoon
comedy
drama
horror

WORKBOOK PAGE 140

UNIT 15 READING

1. c
2. b
3. a
4. b
5. d
6. c

WORKBOOK PAGE 141

A. WHICH FORM OF IDENTIFICATION?

1. e
2. b
3. f
4. a
5. d
6. c

B. WHICH FORM?

1. driver's license
2. an employee I.D. badge
3. student I.D. card
4. proof of residence
5. passport

WORKBOOK PAGE 142

A. WHO, WHAT, WHERE?

Which branch?	Who?
legislative	representatives senators
executive	president vice-president
judicial	chief justice Supreme Court justices

Which building?	What do they do?
Capitol Building	make the laws
White House	enforce the laws
Supreme Court Building	explain the laws

B. TRUE OR FALSE?

1. T
2. T
3. F
4. T
5. F

WORKBOOK PAGE 143

A. WHICH IS CORRECT?

1. Preamble
2. law
3. ten
4. guarantees
5. established
6. 1st
7. women

B. WHICH AMENDMENT?

1. 1st
2. 16th
3. 19th
4. 13th
5. 26th
6. 15th

C. THE 1ST AMENDMENT

1. b
2. a
3. d
4. c

WORKBOOK PAGE 144

A. WHEN ARE THEY?

1. c
2. f
3. e
4. b
5. i
6. g
7. h
8. d
9. a

B. HOLIDAY TRADITIONS

1. Valentine's
2. New Year's
3. Halloween
4. Thanksgiving
5. Independence
6. Ramadan
7. Martin Luther King, Jr.
8. Christmas

C. HOLIDAYS AND THE CALENDAR

1. January
2. last
3. Thursday

WORKBOOK PAGE 145

UNIT 16 READING

1. d
2. b
3. c
4. b
5. a
6. d

This correlation indicates how the activity pages in the *Word by Word Basic Lifeskills Workbook* coordinate with the lessons in the *Word by Word Basic Picture Dictionary* Second Edition.

Basic Picture Dictionary Pages	Workbook Pages	Basic Picture Dictionary Pages	Workbook Pages	Basic Picture Dictionary Pages	Workbook Pages
2–3	1–2	72–83	51	168–169	99
4–5	3–4	84–85	52	170–171	100
6–7	5	86–87	53	172–173	101–102
2–7	6	88–89	54	174–175	103
8–9	7	90–91	55	176–177	104
10–11	8	92–93	56	178–179	105
12–13	9	84–95	57	180–181	106
14–15	10	84–95	58	182–183	107
16–17	11	96–97	59	184–185	108
18–19	12	98–99	60	186–187	109
20–21	13	100–101	61	162–187	110
8–21	14	102–103	62	188–189	111
22–23	15	104–105	63	190–191	112
24–25	16	106–107	64	192–193	113
26–27	17	108–109	65	194–195	114
28–29	18	110–111	66	196–197	115
30–31	19	112–113	67	198–199	116
32–33	20	114	68	200–201	117
22–33	21	115	69	202–203	118
34	22	116–117	70	188–203	119
35	23	118–119	71	204–205	120
36–37	24	120–121	72	206–207	121
38	25	122–123	73	208–209	122
39	26	124–125	74	210–211	123
40–41	27	126–127	75	212–213	124
42–43	28	96–127	76	214–215	125
34–43	29	128–129	77	216–217	126
44–45	30	130–131	78	218–219	127
46–47	31	132–133	79	220–221	128
48–49	32	134–135	80	222–223	129
50–51	33	136–137	81	204–223	130
52–53	34	138–139	82	224–225	131
54–55	35	140–141	83	226–227	132
56–57	36	142–143	84	228–229	133
58–59	37	144–145	85	230–231	134
60–61	38	146–147	86	224–231	135
62–63	39	148–149	87	232–233	136
64–65	40	150–151	88	234–235	137
66–67	41	128–151	89	236–237	138
68–69	42	152–153	90	238–239	139
70–71	43	154–155	91	232–239	140
44–71	44	156–157	92	240–241	141
72–73	45	158–159	93	242–243	142
74–75	46	160–161	94	244–245	143
76–77	47	152–161	95	246–247	144
78–79	48	162–163	96	240–247	145
80–81	49	164–165	97		
82–83	50	166–167	98		